A L.I.F.E. Recovery Guide for Recovery from Addictive Behavior

A Workbook for Living in Freedom Everyday

Dr. Ralph Spiller

Core Material By

Dr. Mark Laaser

Table of Contents

One	Accountability and Humility
Two	Accountability and Expressing Feelings
Three	Accountability and Stating your Needs
Four	Accountability and Your Army
Five	Accountability and Internal Warfare
Six	Accountability and Rebuilding
Seven	Accountability and Garbage
Eight	Accountability and Home
Nine	Accountability and Preparation
Ten	Accountability and Boundaries
Eleven	Accountability and Fellowship
Twelve	Accountability and Motivations
Thirteen	Accountability and Building While Defending
Fourteen	Accountability and Positive Things
Fifteen	Accountability and Your L.I.F.E.
Sixteen	Accountability and Commitment
Seventeen	Accountability and External Warfare
Eighteen	Accountability and Sacrifice

L.I.F.E. Recovery's Vision and Mission

Since 2000, the Lord has blessed L.I.F.E. Recovery International with increasing and escalating fruit from the materials within its L.I.F.E. Recovery Guides. This testimony developed into "recovery best practices" known as the LRM, the L.I.F.E. Recovery Model, endorsed by Mark Laaser, PhD, the foremost Christian authority on sexual addiction recovery and author of the L.I.F.E. Recovery Guide for sexual addiction. The LRM can be read and downloaded in its entirety from the website http://www.freedomeveryday.org/lrm.

As individuals came to L.I.F.E. Recovery seeking freedom from sexual addiction, the L.I.F.E. Recovery Guide's recovery principles addressed every dependency the addict struggled with, not just sexual sin. As the application and fruit grew, the Father expanded our vision and gave us a desire to bring L.I.F.E. Principles to all those wresting with dependency so they may also Live In Freedom Everyday by uncovering and healing core wounds that drive their addictions.

As addiction research advances and brings new recovery applications, L.I.F.E. Recovery will continue to stay abreast of research and effective recovery practices and will be found faithful to adhere to biblical truths while passing on knowledge and practices that expedite the recovery process.

This "L.I.F.E. Recovery Guide for Recovery from Addictive Behavior," just as its sexual addiction predecessor, paves the way for Christ-centered core issue treatment. L.I.F.E. Recovery is grateful to have Dr. Ralph Spiller, a known author and speaker in the area of addiction recovery, as the author of this L.I.F.E. Recovery Guide for Recovery from Addictive Behavior. Each series of the L.I.F.E. Recovery Guides has been written by known and respected experts in recovery ministry, each with the cooperation and blessings of Dr. Laaser.

Statement of Faith

L.I.F.E. Recovery International believes that the Scriptures of the Old and New Testaments are completely inspired by God and should be the single authority for instructions in healthy and godly living. We believe in one God who exists in three persons - the Father, the Son, and the Holy Spirit. We believe that Jesus Christ is the only begotten Son of the Father, and that He was conceived by the Holy Spirit, born of the Virgin Mary, and lived a sinless life. He was crucified and buried and rose from the dead to sit at the right hand of the Father. He will come again to the earth in power and glory. We believe that only through true faith in Jesus Christ as Savior and Lord can a person enter the Kingdom of Heaven. We believe that God's Holy Spirit empowers us to grow closer to our Heavenly Father and to obediently walk in His will.

We further believe that a successful recovery journey requires transformation based on the principles in this L.I.F.E. Recovery Guide and the surrender of your life to Jesus Christ.

Foreword

Addiction and other compulsive behavioral choices (e.g. gambling, eating disorders, et. al.) are all too common in our society, and are as prevalent within the Christian community as they are in society at large. All of these problems have been colloquially referred to as addictions. It is the opinion of this author that addiction is the core issue with various modes of expression. With media exposure, addiction and "rehab" have taken on a "badge of honor" of sorts that has become a common cancer within today's culture, and the church is certainly, but sadly, not exempt. The number of people struggling with addiction in one or more modes of expression has become a major blight on the familial and social fabric of our communities and our nation leading to family deterioration and collapse, negative economic impact upon families and industrial production, and moral corruption that threatens our very existence due to two main factors: the prevalence and availability of resources, and a saturated media that tends to "glorify" the use of alcohol, drugs, gambling, sex, and other unhealthy and compulsive behaviors. Dr. Mark Laaser, author of the L.I.F.E. Recovery Guide for sexual addiction, has commented that our entire society is being abused by this onslaught. Many of these same people desperately long to be free from their bondage and intensely desire to live in integrity and sobriety. They want to experience genuine L.I.F.E.-- Living In Freedom Everyday.

This "L.I.F.E. Recovery Guide for Recovery from Addictive Behavior" joins a series of workbooks dedicated to helping God's people live free from the bondage of addiction, and equipping them to walk in His unconditional love.

The L.I.F.E. Recovery support group program offers Christ-centered and relationally oriented groups that incorporate spiritual discipline, small group accountability, and ongoing prayer and support for those struggling with various forms of addiction.

L.I.F.E. Recovery Groups are support groups, not therapy groups. While there is much within each of the L.I.F.E. Recovery Guides and the recommended recovery materials to help the struggler identify and deal with the wounds from the past, we also encourage individual therapy to address root issues that often lead to unhealthy choices regarding solutions to relieve the pain from the wounds. A trained counselor to guide the healing of core wounds is vital to living in freedom everyday.

The ongoing support, so critical to the process of transformation, comes from the networking of lives through L.I.F.E. Recovery Groups. These groups involve real relationships - open, transparent, and accountable connections with fellow strugglers. L.I.F.E. Recovery Groups value confidentiality and maintain an absolute commitment to provide a safe atmosphere for complete honesty and complete acceptance, where members are embraced in an attitude of love and forgiveness from others sharing common struggles; this sense of safety and freedom from condemnation is critical to successful group functioning. All of these components "guide" the group members toward Christ-centered life choices, according to the conviction that our true identity is found in the freedom and grace that only Jesus can offer.

Acknowledgements

First, I am grateful to God for the opportunity given to me to participate in the efforts of L.I.F.E. Recovery International toward the recovery, and regeneration, of those who have succumbed to the darkness of addictive behaviors. This work will also be useful to those who seek to assist these individuals lost in their addiction. A work of this nature, if it is to be a work worthy of our LORD's use, must have the power of prayer to develop and sustain it. I wish to thank my God for His guiding hand, and the many who have provided prayer support to produce the work you now hold in your hand.

Also, I thank Bob and Johna Hale for their invitation to develop this Guide to Recovery for those affected by, what we shall call, Addictive Behavior. It has been their continued support and encouragement in the revision of the original work to address Sexual Addiction that has been the most significant contribution in the production of this workbook. The original work from which much of the material in this workbook is drawn was authored by Dr. Mark Laaser. To Dr. Mark Laaser I give the greatest appreciation for allowing his work to be modified to broaden the scope of application of the principles that are the framework of his work to now be retained in the production of this work. I thank, also, other members of the L.I.F.E. Recovery team, Sue Moore and others, for their time spent in review and editing the manuscript.

A project of this magnitude requires the input, support, and prayers of all mentioned here. To God be the glory for any and all success that may result from the use of the material presented here between these covers.

Rev. Ralph H. Spiller, Jr., PhD, LMHC
January 2012

Acknowledgements from L.I.F.E. Recovery

Our deep gratitude goes to those who have also helped produce this work: For the cover design, to Katie Palamaro, and to Sue Moore for her expertise in structuring and managing the project and its components and her unwavering commitment to seeing it completed. Special thanks to Nancy Yacher for her expert editing and to Sandra Mackey for formatting the *L.I.F.E. Recovery Guide for Recovery from Addictive Behavior* into its current form.

In addition, thanks to the members of L.I.F.E. Recovery's core leadership team, who have contributed not only hours of dedicated work, but the rich wisdom of their experience in support group ministry. Of course, the greatest thanks go to Dr. Mark Laaser, for his original work in developing L.I.F.E. Recovery's methodology, and to Dr. Ralph Spiller for his commitment to adapting that original material to address the addictive condition in all its manifestations. We are grateful for their willingness to share what they have learned from God about Living in Freedom Everyday.

Bob and Johna Hale
L.I.F.E. Recovery International
2012

Registration with L.I.F.E. Recovery

We encourage all groups using this L.I.F.E. Recovery Guide to become a ***Registered L.I.F.E. Recovery Group***. Registering your L.I.F.E. Recovery Group with L.I.F.E. Recovery International ensures effective recovery literacy through the time tested best practices shown in the LRM, the L.I.F.E. Recovery Model (http://www.freedomeveryday.org/lrm). Registration also entitles your group facilitator to access discounts on workbooks and opens communication links for information about conferences, workshops, and leadership and ministry training. Through newsletters and the L.I.F.E. Recovery website, your group facilitators will have access to materials and information to help your L.I.F.E. Recovery Group grow and to expand your recovery ministry within your church and your community. Registered L.I.F.E. Recovery Groups will also be listed in our network of L.I.F.E. Recovery Groups, so those looking for help in your community can find it, and your group members will never be without needed support when away from home. Finally, by registering, one by one, groups will be furthering the work of L.I.F.E. Recovery International helping to make this support group ministry available in additional churches and communities across the country and around the world.

To find out more information, to start a L.I.F.E. Recovery Group, or to become a Registered L.I.F.E. Recovery Group, checkout the ministry's website, call toll-free, or write for more information. We would love to welcome you and start you on the journey toward Living In Freedom Everyday in God's unconditional love.

L.I.F.E. Recovery International   **866-408-LIFE (866-408-5433)**
P.O. Box 952317
Lake Mary, FL 32795   **www.freedomeveryday.org**

A L.I.F.E. RECOVERY GUIDE FOR RECOVERY FROM ADDICTIVE BEHAVIOR INTRODUCTION

SPIRITUAL DOCTRINE: If God can heal disease, then He can heal me!

As a Christian, you may be wondering why you should submit yourself to a "man-made" recovery program. Why not, instead, spend your time praying for an instantaneous deliverance brought about by an outpouring of Gods power? After all, the Bible speaks of the POWER of the Holy Spirit that works within you, the Bible says that God did not give you a spirit of fear but of POWER, the Bible says that the same POWER that raised Jesus from the dead resides inside you...so why the need for a PROCESS?

Well, this is a very fair question with a very simple answer. The truth is, nearly every addict that comes to our ministry has been praying intensely and often for God to deliver them from their addiction. This is a good thing to do and therefore it is something we encourage. God DOES pour out His power to bring healing to addicts. His power to heal addictions, however, does not strike once like a lightning bolt; it flows continually like a river. It is a power that can only be experienced through simple, authentic Christian fellowship. It requires the conduits of transparency, confession, debriefing, and relearning...all of which can only be experienced through community. So it's not a question of power vs. process; it's an embracing of God's power *through* process.

God often heals cancer and other physical ailments instantaneously because doing so does not compromise the overall health of our physical body. In the case of addiction, however, an instantaneous healing *would* compromise our overall emotional and mental health. Such an experience would teach us that our deepest emotional conflicts (which are at the core of our addictive condition) can be healed in isolation and this is not possible. This would be a lesson that is counter-productive to God's design for us, as He has created us for intimacy – with Himself, with His Son Jesus and with each other. We were wounded in relationship; therefore God has chosen to bring healing through relationship. Of course He could bring instant relief of the craving, but years of experience and biblical evidence indicates that He has chosen to bring wholeness through our active participation in a transparent Christian community. If in this transparent environment we address core wounds that have hindered our spiritual maturity we will remove the tendency to switch addictions altogether. We will talk more about this later. Meanwhile, welcome to a L.I.F.E. of recovery!

FAMILY SYSTEMS: This looks familiar...

If there is one thing you need to understand about addiction it's this: Coping or self-medicating doesn't need an invitation...it only needs an opportunity.

At one time, you were an innocent, unsuspecting child. You, most likely, weren't guided through the experiences in your life that opened the door for a need to escape. Your family, much like any other, may have been unreliable and unskilled themselves to bear the challenge of making it through the day's circumstances. Maybe the best model you saw was how to simply survive. Perhaps you learned at an early age that life cannot be trusted to turn out well so you made your way through the turmoil by using any opportunity to cope and escape the reality. Yet this was your home, your family, your relationships and extended family. In fact, there is an entire psychological discipline about this. It was originally formulated by Dr. Murray Bowen and is called **family systems theory**. As Dr. Bowen explains,

> *A family is a system in which each member has a role to play and rules to respect. Members of the system are expected to respond to each other in a certain way according to their role, which is determined by relationship agreements. Within the boundaries of the system, patterns develop as certain family member's behavior is caused by and causes other family member's behaviors in predictable ways.*

In short, Dr. Bowen believed that you, as a person, cannot be understood (or understand yourself) apart from your family system. This is true because of the following widely recognized principle: early influences operate to shape future behavior. And the majority of your early influences came to you through your family system. Unfortunately, the chaos and injury some of us experienced within our family systems set us up to be vulnerable to compulsive and addictive behavior as adults. Some family systems can even go so far as *modeling* this type of behavior for us! You can see scriptural reference in Exodus 20 for this type of generational curse. Is it any wonder that our addictive condition looks familiar?

FRAGMENTATION: I think I'm going mad…

Your dependency can certainly be driving you to **fragmentation.** According to Christopher J. Charleton, M.A., LCSW, a licensed clinical therapist and president of InterAct Counseling PLLC, a state-of-the-art Christian treatment facility in Rochester, NY, fragmentation is a result of disintegration, which is in direct contrast to God's design of integration. That sounds a bit confusing to me, so think of it this way: you were created in the image of the Triune God; God the Father, God the Son and God the Holy Spirit. The Trinity is a perfect example of integration; each aspect of the trinity is in union with the others, glorifying and reflecting each other's true value in relationship. Similarly, as someone created in God's image, you were also designed to be integrated in relationships, thereby illuminating the true value of yourself and others.

The problem is, your family of origin experiences challenged your belief in God's design and skewed your perception of the value of being integrated in community. When your relationships were subsequently compromised (or even avoided altogether), disintegration occurred. Now, here's the main point: **fragmentation perceives both integration and disintegration to be true**…and an internal war between intimacy and isolation ensues. The apostle Paul said it this way, *"I don't understand what I do. For what I want to do* (intimacy) *I don't do, and the very thing I hate* (isolation) *I do. Now if I do what I do not want to do it is no longer I who does it, but it is sin* (dependency) *living in me"* (additions mine). So then, this L.I.F.E. Recovery Guide you're holding, its Principles and Journal Assignments, will prove to be a huge benefit by giving you the tools to examine yourself and your experiences. After all, don't we want to live in freedom? It's our skewed perception that fuels the war between intimacy and isolation in the first place.

ADDICTIVE CONDITION: So one more time…What's my problem?

It's not alcohol. Alcohol does not create alcoholics. It's not pornography. Pornography doesn't create sex addicts. Neither is your addictive condition a box of Twinkies or a deck of cards or a freshly rolled joint or an eighty hour a week job.

The problem is your underlying addictive *condition* and it consists of a whole host of issues; neurochemical imbalances, arrested development, unresolved emotional wounds, fragmentation, and an incapacity for emotional wholeness and intimacy. These are the things that create addicts. The problem does not resemble a pair of dice, a sexual encounter, or a box of chocolates, although it likes to play with things like these…especially when you are in pain. Given enough pain and enough opportunity, these things then become the focus of your addictive *behavior.*

In recovery terms, your addictive behavior is simply your attempt to medicate the pain of some past trauma or relational wounding that has not been resolved, and the fact that it remains unresolved becomes the (often subconscious) excuse for continuing in your addictive behavior. It is a self-perpetuating cycle of destruction. And on top of that, Satan is always there to cooperate, using and intensifying your addictive behavior and further disabling your ability to have relationships with those you care about (or even with God Himself). Your problem, your addictive condition, is your enemy and is used by the enemy to bring devastation to your life. Nevertheless, your addictive condition, your coping method or self-medicating always masquerades as your friend.

You very likely found your method(s) of coping amidst the turmoil of your family system. Acting out was fun and even helpful at first, but as you continually fed your addictive condition through years the behavior became pretty burdensome. And so you're here, in need of a community of people who can help you to more clearly identify what's driving your addictive condition and help you through God's healing power to uncover and heal those wounds, for good!

Oh…so what you are really saying is I just need to get sober.

Nope.

Huh?

Sobriety is measured in time. You will be deemed "sober" when you have not engaged in addictive behaviors for twenty-four hours, or a week, a month, etc. That's a great start, but it is not enough.

Your addictive condition is clever, resourceful and sinister, and it will let you be sober for a while if it means it can hang around for the long haul. Even Satan, after unsuccessfully tempting Jesus in the desert, simply waited for a more opportune time. Your addictive condition will do the same.

What you need is wholeness. Sobriety is a part of the equation but by itself sobriety does not equal wholeness. Being whole means you are practicing real intimacy. It means you are self-aware and capable of modulating negative emotions through healthy means. It means you are present in the moment instead of being lost inside your head. It means you no longer hide behind "fine." Being whole means God is having His way with you, and as a result you are being transformed inside and out. The point is, you can be sober and still be acting out of your addictive condition. But when you are whole your addictive condition is not only ***not*** driving--but has no opportunity to re-establish itself and get a seat within you.

Patrick Carnes, PhD, a pioneer in addiction recovery, has stated; "more than 87 percent of addicts come from disengaged families--a family environment in which family members are detached, uninvolved, or emotionally absent. *All compulsive and addictive behaviors are signs of significant intimacy disorder and the inability to get needs met in healthy ways.*" Carnes' statement suggests the importance of being connected, involved and emotionally present in order to get your needs met in healthy ways, and since this hasn't been modeled you have to learn how this is done. There are three critical elements that promote this growth: managing distressing emotions, support and disclosure, and cognitive processing. Each are provided in a L.I.F.E. Recovery Group setting, where you learn to express feelings relating to an injury; including anger, anxiety and sadness, and to process that pain. This learning to express your feelings and to process pain is a very fundamental part of your recovery. A separate resource, the L.I.F.E. Grieving Guide, has been created for just this purpose, and you will be encouraged to go through that work at an appropriate time in your journey.

By joining a local L.I.F.E. Recovery Group and completing the work that is found in the L.I.F.E. Recovery Guide you are holding, we believe you can achieve wholeness. Accomplishing this will require a lot of consistent effort on your part, but know this; there are thousands of men and women throughout the world who can give testimony to the fact that it was the community and self-discovery they found through L.I.F.E. Recovery that God used to set them free. You **can** Live In Freedom Everyday! Welcome to L.I.F.E.!

How to Use This L.I.F.E. Recovery Guide

Hopefully, you'll use this workbook because someone at a L.I.F.E. Recovery Group recommended it. You've made a decision to do something about coping and medicating your pain and have found a L.I.F.E. Recovery Group, which means you'll have the strength of the fellowship of others to help you get started. Lean on them and learn how to listen. (Realize that your own best thinking got you here. Open yourself to learning a different way.) Quiet your mind. Remind Satan that he's lost the battle with you and should just shut up and leave you alone. You don't want to listen to him, because you're recognizing he's the father of lies. Make a firm commitment *not* to listen to him again.

Your Private Journal

The first thing you'll need to do is get a journal of some sort. It could be as simple as a spiral bound notebook, or it could be a fancy journal found at bookstores and office supply stores. It may even be a three-ring binder so that you can add as many pages as you need. Whatever its form, your personal journal should be something you feel completely comfortable writing in. L.I.F.E. Recovery made a decision not to put a great deal of space in this workbook for you to write in so that you can refer back to this material over and over again. The plan is for you to do most of the writing assignments in your journal instead of in this workbook, but sometimes you'll notice short-answer space is provided for convenience. Each assignment contains some discussion about the Principle being presented and the thought processes necessary to complete the particular writing assignment(s) within that Principle. The actual assignment instructions are clearly marked within the discussion content to be sure it's evident what you should record in your journal.

Be certain to put your name on your journal. It will become *your* **sacred** document, and no one else should see it unless *you* decide to share it. Do you remember how some old diaries had locks on them to protect the contents? Get that idea in your mind. This is your journal for you to record your answers and thoughts with complete honesty. You don't want anyone else reading it uninvited.

Your journal should be a hand written document. It should not reside on a computer. The computer has gotten many of us in trouble and it may not be healthy to work on the computer as you begin your healing. Also, you will find as you write by hand that you will have more time to reflect.

I've observed over the years that others may want to look at your journal. Your spouse will probably be one of them. Don't be hard on them for wanting to see what you've written. They may have been wounded by your addictions and want to know the truth. They may be angry with you and feel they have a right to read your journal.

But believe me: **It's a healthy boundary to keep private the contents of this diary about your life**. Don't be afraid to set this boundary. (Another important suggestion is to keep your journal out of plain sight, so that others aren't unnecessarily tempted to invade your privacy.) *The writing that you do in your journal is between you and God.* Pray for the power of the Holy Spirit to help you be honest and thorough and to guard your writings from unauthorized eyes.

You may at times want to show what you've written to your spouse, to others, to your sponsor, group members, pastor, or therapist. That choice is acceptable if you decide it's for *your* benefit. But please know that's *your* decision, OK? Refuse to be pressured into sharing your journal, especially by your spouse.

Organization of L.I.F.E. Recovery Guide Material

Each of the Seven Principles is divided into three assignments. Every time a L.I.F.E. Recovery Group meets it will focus on one of the seven Principles as the theme for that meeting. Each L.I.F.E. Recovery Group, though, will be attended by members who are at different stages in their healing journey. Some may have years of sobriety, while others may be coming to their first meeting. **L.I.F.E. Recovery Groups should always be open to new members who are coming for the first time**. No one can predict God's timing about when a person may finally decide to seek help. Therefore, every time a L.I.F.E. Recovery Group focuses on a Principle, each person in the group should be working one of the three assignments within that Principle.

Each assignment is designed to take you deeper in the work of a Principle. Assignment One consistently is somewhat basic — it's the core and the foundation of that Principle. Each Assignment Two asks you to work on the next core elements. Finally, Assignment Three takes you into deeper understandings of a Principle.

L.I.F.E. Recovery Guide Assignment Flow

The flow of the L.I.F.E. Recovery Guide assignments is such that you'll work on the assignments in succession as formatted in this L.I.F.E. Recovery Guide. The plan is that you'll work on all <u>seven of the first assignments first</u>, then all seven of the <u>second</u> assignments, and finally all seven of the <u>third</u> assignments. This schedule means that after completing Principle One, Assignment One, you'll move on to Principle <u>Two</u>, Assignment One. When you've completed Principle Seven, Assignment One, you'll begin Principle One, Assignment <u>Two</u>, as arranged in this workbook.

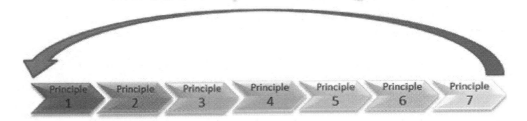

Introducing Newcomers to Assignments

Introductory or Grieving Work

Principle Work – Continuous Cycle

For the purpose of clarifying the introduction of newcomers to L.I.F.E. Guide assignments, Dr. Laaser writes the following statement.

"We've always suggested that all participants be on the same principle yet they can be on different assignments."

As suggested by Dr. Laaser, the main group continually cycles through Principles 1 -7 emphasizing all levels of assignments relevant to the participants that are present. Because newcomers are asked to complete introductory work before beginning the L.I.F.E. Recovery Guide assignments, the following approach illustrates our recommendation to introduce participants to the workbook assignments, please read the following.

Orientation or Grieving Guide - Introductory Work:
Unless there are other attendees in the Introductory Group, the newcomer works independently on those assignments while attending the main Principle group, which then allows for the discussion of their homework in small group. After completion of Introductory work, the newcomer then begins the Principle work in the main group.

Principle Work (Main Group):
Although the newcomer attends the main Principle group without interruption, due to the foundation building aspect of the L.I.F.E. Recovery Guide assignments and the continuous cycle of the Principles in the main group, the newcomer should take this opportunity to observe the group and wait to begin the material when the group cycles back to Principle 1.

Continually working through the Principles

As recommended in the LRM (L.I.F.E. Recovery Model), the 21 assignments should be cycled continuously for complete and effective recovery as the depth of this material will speak to wherever you are in your recovery at that time.

There are a total of twenty-one assignments. This outline doesn't necessarily mean you'll only need 21 weeks to go through the L.I.F.E. Recovery Guide. It may take you several weeks to do just one of the assignments. Work at a pace that's comfortable for you. *Being thorough is more important than being quick.* Your sponsor or your group can help you know how you're doing. Remember that at each meeting you'll be working on an assignment related to the Principle being discussed that night. This format technically means you could work several different times on the same assignment in a Principle, *but that those times could be seven weeks apart.*

Let's assume, for example, that you're working on Principle One, Assignment One. You start on this lesson the first time your L.I.F.E. Recovery Group is addressing that Principle. The next week you move to Principle <u>Two</u>, Assignment One. You may not be completely finished with Principle One, Assignment One, and that's fine. You can tag it and come back later to finish. At this point, you just keep going through the L.I.F.E. Recovery Guide and move on to Principle Two so that you'll be on task with the others. When the group cycles back to Principle One after seven weeks, you take up where you left off in Assignment One. Following this slower format might take you a year to work through the entire workbook for the first time. That's fine. Others of you may want to march right through and get all the work of an assignment done in one week, which means you'll go through the entire workbook during the first 21 weeks. Everyone is different. Recovery isn't a race or a competition; it's a transforming way of life.

This L.I.F.E. Recovery Guide is a growing, changing document. You may work through it a number of times in the course of your healing journey. In fact, I hope you will. The inventory you complete in Principle Four, for example, will expand as you grow in your journey of self-awareness and honesty. It will be more complete when you have several years of sobriety as compared to when you're just starting out in recovery.

Your L.I.F.E. Recovery Group will concentrate on the Seven Principles of transformation. My hope is that all of the exercises in this Guide will challenge you. Some of them may overwhelm you. There's a tremendous amount of work outlined in these pages. At times you may be tempted to skip some exercises or skimp on writing your answers. I pray you'll persevere and complete each assignment. **A key point to remember is that rigorous and thorough work is the best way to start healing.**

You may discover you fill more than one journal as you go through this material. Good for you! Journaling is one of the best emotional and spiritual tools available, and working in this L.I.F.E. Recovery Guide may be your start of this wonderful spiritual discipline. Consider the great writers who have written journals throughout their lives. As you read the L.I.F.E.

Recovery Guide and study Scripture for the rest of your life, writing your thoughts and feelings may become like a friend that helps you grow continually.

As you'll notice, there are other suggested readings along the way, which are intended to be helpful in your work here. I certainly don't claim that this effort is "exhaustive." It's the most complete workbook I'm aware of, but it's only one book. A workbook is a tool which is designed for your benefit. If there are other materials that help with your transformation process, that's great. Use them to support your journey to freedom and healing. We have found that reading supplemental material is essential to the LRM. Self-education is necessary to the recovery process, but supplemental material should *never* replace or interrupt the recommended L.I.F.E. Recovery Guide assignment cycles.

Supplemental materials provide valuable information and are suggested to increase the understanding of the origins, consequences and behaviors of addiction and should complement consistent attendance in a L.I.F.E. Recovery Group. Supplemental materials are not sufficient to replace the L.I.F.E. Recovery Group's involvement in the recovery process. In addition to utilizing the L.I.F.E. Recovery Training as supplemental material, here are some of L.I.F.E. endorsed authors to build your library and understanding, Patrick Carnes, Mark Laaser, Debbie Laaser, Christopher Charleton, Richard Blankenship, Marnie Ferree, Russell Willingham, Cloud and Townsend. To see a complete list on our website go to http://www.freedomeveryday.org.

You can also ask another group member who has been working a recovery program for some time to help you. Ask those in your L.I.F.E. Recovery Group for their contact information so you can call on them if you have questions. As you progress, you'll become more comfortable with the practice of asking for help.

Most of all, I pray that the God of all peace and understanding will keep your heart and mind focused on Christ Jesus throughout this journey.

L.I.F.E. Recovery Group Meeting Guide

Identity of Groups

Because this series of workbooks is sponsored by L.I.F.E. Recovery, most of the support groups which use this material will call their groups "L.I.F.E. Recovery Groups." There are other groups that use this material that have developed across the country. Some of those groups may choose to identify themselves by that or another name, but we strongly encourage groups to become a Registered L.I.F.E. Recovery Group in order to maintain reasonable consistency as well as for the enhancement and escalation of recovery efforts across the USA and around the world. What your group calls itself isn't as important as *how* you conduct your meeting. All groups calling themselves "L.I.F.E." Groups should follow these meeting guidelines and leadership principles. For the remainder of this chapter, I'll refer to groups as "L.I.F.E. Recovery Groups."

Christian therapists could use the material in these L.I.F.E. Recovery Guides to conduct a therapy group. In such cases, the meeting guide may not be necessary, as therapists will know how to competently conduct a group. An important principle, however, is that L.I.F.E. Recovery doesn't encourage individuals to use this material alone, without being part of a group. As you'll see, this work is intended to be applied in fellowship, not in isolation. That intention doesn't mean, of course, that you won't do the specific exercises in most of the assignments alone. They're meant, though, to be processed with others in some form of accountability.

Group Format

Every L.I.F.E. Recovery Group should follow a standard format. Experience indicates that meetings that don't use a standard format can easily become free-for-alls. They're vulnerable to the moods and distractions of the moment. They're also vulnerable to the more dominant personalities in the group. (Many times those who seek to dominate are the least healthy ones in the group.) All groups need strong facilitators, and a few individuals in every group will provide that. It's not fair to them, though, if only one or two always have to facilitate the group. If the safety guidelines and meeting format listed below are followed, most of the issues about facilitating and dominating individuals are eliminated.

L.I.F.E. Recovery recommends the following outline. Each group or facilitator may modify the outline to best suit the group's unique needs, but *groups should modify with care*, because once the format is established, a group should stick to it consistently.

Consider duplicating the Meeting Format and the various Readings and laminating them or placing them in sheet protectors for ease of use during meetings.

L.I.F.E. Recovery Group Meeting Format
(Note: Italics provide instructions or information not intended to be read aloud.)

1. Opening Introduction and Prayer

Opening statement by the facilitator:

"My name is _____, and I am healing from using dependencies to escape pain. This is the *(state the time of the meeting, e.g. the Monday night)* **L.I.F.E. Recovery Group, and I welcome each person here. I commend you on your commitment to be pure before God. This is a closed meeting, which means that only those seeking their own personal recovery may attend."**

Opening prayer: ***The facilitator prays or the group joins in saying a prayer of their choosing, such as the Serenity Prayer or the Lord's Prayer.***

2. Group Introductions

Facilitator says:
   "I invite everyone to introduce yourself as we go around the room."
Each person introduces himself as the facilitator did:
   "My name is _____, and I am healing from using..."
A newcomer may choose to say:
   "My name is _____, and I'm a newcomer."

3. Welcome New Members

L.I.F.E. Recovery Groups are always open to new members or attendees who are seeking help. The facilitator says:

"Is anyone attending a meeting for your first time? *(Pause for show of hands.)* **We welcome newcomers and we're glad you've come. At your first meeting you aren't expected to talk, but we'll be honored if you do. There may be opportunities for you to share either in this larger group session or after we break up into smaller groups. But most importantly, this is a time for you as a newcomer to listen and start feeling safe.**

"We believe an important practice for everyone on the journey of transformation is to use a sponsor to help work this program. If you'd like a temporary sponsor for the next week(s), see me after the meeting. Also, if you have any questions about our L.I.F.E. Recovery Group and how it functions, please see me after the meeting."

4. Readings

Standard readings, which are printed in the L.I.F.E. Recovery Guide after this "Meeting Format" section, are shared at every meeting. The facilitator selects readers and distributes the readings before the meeting starts, if possible.

The facilitator says, **"I've asked** *(name)*_____ **to read the** *(name of reading)*_____ **."**

Those who've agreed to read share the material below:

> **Mission Statement** *(or a part of the Mission Statement) - and/or -*
> **The Seven Principles** *- and/or -*
> **The Seven "Cs"** *- and/or -*
> **Safety Guidelines and Group Covenant** *(<u>always</u> read if newcomers are present)*
> **Nehemiah Principles** *(any appropriate part of Principles1-18)*

5. Offering

An offering container is passed around the group as the facilitator says:

> **"There are no dues or fees for membership and all are welcome regardless of their ability to make a contribution. However, all L.I.F.E. Recovery Groups are self-supporting. We pay for our own materials, rent** *(if applicable)* **and other expenses, and we contribute to L.I.F.E. Recovery International. We suggest $5 weekly as a contribution to your own healing and to ensure others have access to the help that you've found. Like an offering at a church, you're not required to give, and you're certainly free to give more than this suggested amount."**

6. Business

The facilitator leads the group in any discussion of old and new business. Old business includes matters such as meeting times and places, and ordering of materials. New business includes matters such as special but related events outside of the group, or any announcement of matters pertaining to the group's well-being.

Note that all decisions are made through the consensus of group members and must be consistent with the policies of L.I.F.E. Recovery. When in doubt, check with the national office.

The facilitator says:

> **"Is there any old business we need to discuss?** *(pause)*
> **"Is there any new business or announcements that affect the group as a whole?"**

7. Discussion of Principle

By prior arrangement, someone will have been asked to either make a presentation or lead a discussion on the Principle being considered that night. This presentation should be limited to no more than 20 minutes.

The facilitator says:
   "*(Name of member)*_____ **will now lead us in discussing Principle** *(number)*___, **which is** _____*(read text of Principle)*_____."

8. Small Group Discussion

Dividing into Groups:

This is a time of accountability, confession, and building relationships. Depending on the size of the total group, everyone counts off in such a way that small groups are created which consists of four or five persons, including the small group facilitator.

The facilitator says, **"Now we'll divide into (__#__) small groups. We'll count off by** __*(2's, 3's, however many is appropriate)*___ **and I'll start...... One..."** *Everyone counts off.*

The facilitator says, **"The small groups will meet as follows: All the "1's" in Room ___, the "2's" in Room ___,"** *etc.* **"You're now dismissed to go to your small groups. Everyone please be back here for our group closing at** *(time)*_____."

Activity during Groups:

Each breakout group should be led by someone with appropriate experience and sobriety. The small groups meet for one hour, dividing the time equally among the members (no more than 10 minutes per person) according to this outline:

Small Group Format:

- *Feelings check-in (how you're feeling physically, emotionally and spiritually).*
- *A helpful tool to process feelings and identifying contributors is the "I feel _____ about _____ because _____" statement.*
- *Share accountability for "Bottom Lines." See page 65.*
- *Share accountability for "Top Lines"*
- *Get current (share what's going on in your life)*
- *Story time (a member shares part of his story or testimony – 10 minutes)*
- *Prayer requests*
- *Prayer*

The whole group reconvenes for the Celebration of Sobriety and closing.

9. Celebration of Sobriety

After everyone is back together, members are encouraged to report their success and celebrate milestones of recovery. The L.I.F.E. Recovery Group recognizes significant periods of sobriety such as one week, one month, three months, six months, and one year or multiples of years. In addition to "L.I.F.E. Recovery Chips" (available online), which are traditional in Alcoholics Anonymous, the group may provide some other kind of memento, such as a certificate, as recognition of these achievements.

The facilitator asks a group member to lead this celebration, and he says:

"We believe it's affirming to recognize those who are finding the L.I.F.E. of living in freedom everyday for significant periods of time. Is there anyone here who's celebrating one week of sobriety? One month? Three months? Six months? A year? Or multiples of years?"

(Obviously, pause between each question to allow response. If a person comes forward, present the chip, and ask if they'd like a hug, then lead the group in applauding. Those celebrating a year or multiple years of sobriety can be invited to make a few brief comments.)

When all have been honored, the facilitator says:

"Congratulations on the chips you've earned and the chips you hold. We give God the glory!"

10. Closing Comments, Reading, and Prayer

Closing Comments: *The facilitator says:*

"I thank everyone for coming and remind you the next meeting is *(time)*   **. We have schedules of other area L.I.F.E. meetings, as well as phone lists of group members willing to receive calls. If anyone has any unfinished individual business, you're encouraged to talk with your sponsor or accountability group this week.**

<u>Please remember that individual anonymity provides the safety for us to risk exposing our secrets to others and to God's transforming light. Who you saw here and what was said here, let it stay here</u>. "

Reading:

The facilitator says, **"I've asked** *(name)*_____ **to conclude our meeting by reading 'The Hope.'"** *(Appointed person reads material.)*

Prayer:

L.I.F.E. Recovery Groups end each meeting with prayer, again usually the Lord's Prayer or Serenity Prayer, at the facilitator's discretion. The facilitator should then adjourn the formal meeting on schedule, but invite interested men to remain for prayer or fellowship among themselves.

Suggested Time Guidelines for Meeting

The timeline for a standard meeting of approximately two hours looks like this:

Welcome, opening prayer, and introductions	5 minutes
Welcome new members	2 minutes
Share readings	8 minutes
Offering and business discussion	5 minutes
Principle presentation and discussion	20 minutes
(Time to break into small groups)	5 minutes
Small Groups	60 minutes
(Time to return to big group)	5 minutes
Celebration of Sobriety	5 minutes
Reconvene and closing	5 minutes
TOTAL MEETING TIME	*2 hours*

L.I.F.E. Recovery Group Safety Guidelines

It is absolutely essential that every L.I.F.E. Recovery Group be safe. Safety produces the best environment for honesty and fellowship. All group members are responsible for observing these Safety Guidelines, and if they are violated, group members must confront each other in love. If an individual cannot observe the guidelines consistently or after being confronted, he/she will be asked to leave the meeting. The well-being of the entire group is more important than any individual member.

1. It is safe to be honest. We expect all members to tell the truth.

2. It is safe to have feelings. All feelings are acceptable to God and to us.

3. We will allow safe group conversation with no graphic activity descriptions or identify location of places where we engaged in our addictive behavior. We give each other feedback as long as it only reflects our own experience, strength, and hope. Therefore, we begin our feedback with "I," and not with "You." We do not give advice.

4. We do not preach. It is acceptable to share messages of spiritual strength and hope, to quote Scripture, or to make theological statements. We avoid comments that use words like "should," "always," or "never," and expressions such as "God says…," God's will for your life is…or God will be angry if…." We all seek to follow Christ in our own way.

5. We do not shame ourselves or others. We do not put down ourselves or anyone else.

6. Focus on yourself, not on others. We do not blame anyone for our sinful behavior. We take total responsibility for our actions.

7. We abide by the principle of group confidentiality. We do not reveal the identity of other group members or any other personal information outside the group, even to our spouses. There is only one exception to this rule. If anyone discloses feelings or actions that indicate he/she is a possible danger to self or to others, including minor children, we will take all necessary action outside of the L.I.F.E. Recovery Group to report that danger and to ensure others' safety. Even more specifically, we must and will report to the proper authorities any disclosure of past or current unreported child or elder abuse. We are very clear about these exceptions to confidentiality.

Consider duplicating the Meeting Format and the various Readings and laminating them or placing them in sheet protectors for ease of use during meetings.

L.I.F.E. Recovery Group Covenant

To encourage a high level of trust, love, accountability and openness in my *L.I.F.E. Recovery Group*, in order to experience wholeness, healing, purity and freedom in Christ, I covenant with my group's other members to do the following:

I will make attendance at each group session ***a priority***. During this time, I will choose the group first when making decisions about my priorities and time. I will arrive on time, knowing the meeting begins at_____. If I cannot attend, I will call my Group facilitator beforehand to notify them. This helps to hold me accountable in my attendance.

I will commit my time each week to complete the appropriate unit of study in the *L.I.F.E. Recovery Guide **before*** the group session. I will confirm with my group facilitator that I have done the homework. This helps to hold me accountable to my recovery. Homework is an important part of recovery and we need to put time and effort into our recovery. Showing up and just 'drafting' off of the group is unfair not only to the group but to myself.

I will keep confidential all personal information group members share. I will not share matters from the group with any outside person or mention the information as a prayer concern. I understand that **what** I see and what I hear in this place **stays** here when I leave. I understand that breaking confidentiality could result in my being asked to leave the group. I may share with my spouse only those things I have learned about myself by being in the group environment.

I will commit to the following:

- To honesty, openness, a willingness to listen, and readiness to implement new behaviors.
- To reaching out and openly sharing my challenges instead of isolating.
- When I share, I will not be graphic or state names or places that were involved in my sinful behavior.
- To submit to the group to lovingly confront me when I am in denial or sin or am acting co-dependently in my marriage or other relationships.
- To support other group members in their desire to grow emotionally and spiritually.
- To be honest in my actions, thoughts, and emotions as I participate in the group.
- To be patient with other group members as we allow God to work in each of our lives.
- To not give advice or pressure other group members to do what I think is best.
- To inform my group facilitator of any physical or emotional problems that might arise through my participation in the group.
- To spend time with the Lord. This is time for me to hear from God and to get to know Him. This is time in prayer for me and my loved ones.
- To journal faithfully as feelings and memories surface, for God has no time-line as He allows me to feel the emotions I have "stuffed." I know that whatever emotions come, God wants me to feel them. I give myself the grace to feel whatever comes.

- To surrender the changes that come to God, knowing that He will work this for my good. I also agree to surrender my marriage (all relationships) and my coping mechanisms to allow Him to make these necessary changes. I understand I will need to do this daily.

I will seek to honor and observe the group rules. This group is safe, therefore:

1. We can be honest.
2. We can be angry (even at God).
3. We can have conflict.
4. We can be sad, lonely or frightened.
5. We will not put ourselves or others down.
6. We will make no self-righteous statements.
7. We will not blame others; we will take responsibility for our own actions.
8. We will only give feedback when asked.
9. We will practice confidentiality.
10. We will strive to affirm ourselves and others.
11. We will pray for God's presence and guidance in all of our discussion.
12. Group time will be divided among those who have completed homework and ask for time to share. If unable to complete homework, we ask that you listen and not give input.

Please Initial: _____ I acknowledge that the **First Year of Recovery** and the **L.I.F.E. Recovery Model** (LRM) have been explained to me and I understand my active role in recovery. I understand that **L.I.F.E. Recovery** must report or cause a report to be made and cannot keep silent on the grounds of confidentiality or privileged communication in the following areas: • When a disclosure indicates a group participant may cause harm to self. • When a disclosure indicates that a group participant may pose a danger to others (Child abuse, Spouse abuse or Elder abuse).

I have read the above and agree to the articles of this **Covenant** for the L.I.F.E. Support Group.

Signed: _____

Date: _____

The Mission of L.I.F.E.

Ours is a fellowship of Christians who have a sincere desire to abstain from addictive behaviors no matter what form they may take, substances or processes, and to present lives holy and pure before God. Many of us have been trapped in a vicious cycle of coping. Ours has been a life of fantasy, ritual, sin and despair. We have felt out of control. We identify with the words of Paul in Romans 7:19:

> *"I know that nothing good lives in me, that is, in my sinful nature. For I have the desire to do what is good, but I cannot carry it out. For what I do is* **not** *the good I want to do; no, the evil I do* **not** *want to do -- this I keep on doing. What a wretched man I am!"*

We realize our dependencies have grown worse over time. We have been addicted to the high of our lustful appetites and desires, our activities, or our unholy relationships. We have not been able to stop despite the consequences, and we experience great shame.

Ours is a history of broken promises to ourselves and others, violated vows, wounded families, lost jobs, physical pain, financial chaos, spiritual bankruptcy, and even potential death. All through our difficult personal histories, what we truly sought was love and nurturing. We've been angry because we felt unloved, and our hearts burned with unmet needs. We've even been angry with God because He didn't take away our temptations, our pain, or our problems. We have been bored with ourselves, with life, and with others around us. We have substituted our dependencies for love, thinking that the high of these pleasures would erase our true need of communion with God, a relationship with Christ, and genuine connection with healthy others.

Many of us have promised, "This is the last time I'll act out," but it was not. Don't be discouraged. You are not alone. Those of us who have chosen to become honest about our pasts and our emotions are experiencing healing with the help of the Holy Spirit. Many of us have tried to recover through our own thinking and on our own. We've even tried to manipulate God's healing through constant prayer, Bible studies, and church attendance. We are finding that God will help us heal only if we are truly willing to submit to His will by keeping ourselves humble and accountable.

If you desire what we have and are willing to go to any lengths to get it, we invite you to join us in the fellowship of L.I.F.E. - living in freedom everyday - with the help of our all loving and all powerful God, through His Son, Jesus Christ.

Seven Principles for L.I.F.E.

Following are the principles we follow as a path for healing our addictive condition:

1. We admit that we have absolutely no control of our lives, and our coping behaviors have made our lives unmanageable.
2. We believe in God, accept the grace offered through His Son, Jesus Christ, and surrender our lives and our will to Him on a daily basis.
3. We make a list of our sins and weaknesses through a daily personal inventory, and confess these to God in prayer and to a person of spiritual authority.
4. We seek accountability and to build our character as a child of God.
5. We will explore the harm that we have done to others, accept responsibility for our actions or inaction, and seek to make amends for the wrongs we have done.
6. In fellowship with others, we will develop honest, intimate relationships, where we celebrate our progress and continue to address our weaknesses.
7. As we live our lives in sobriety, we will carry the message of Christ's healing power to those who still struggle, and pursue a vision of God's purpose for our lives.

Seven "C's" of Transformation

For some of us it's easier to remember these Principles in the form of Seven "C's:"

1. Conceit is gone.
2. Control is surrendered.
3. Confession is made.
4. Character is changing.
5. Contrition is offered.
6. Consistency is established.
7. Communicating "the hope" is essential.

These principles are a guide on the journey of recovery and not the magical cure. If you're willing to surrender your old way of thinking and your methods of medicating your pain, then you, too, can live in freedom everyday in healthy intimate relationships.

Because we come from different Christian backgrounds and traditions, we do not endorse any particular church or denomination. We have no opinions concerning race, economic or educational background, politics, philosophy, or differences between people.

What we share is a common desire to be totally honest about ourselves, about what we have done, about who we are and how we feel; and about our commitment to remain sober and pure in our relationships. We define sobriety as not only abstinence from addictive behaviors (coping behaviors in an attempt to manage our pain), but also having and promoting healthy relationships with others in ways that honor one another and glorify God. If you sincerely and humbly share these desires, we welcome you in this fellowship to embrace L.I.F.E. - Living In Freedom Everyday.

The Hope of L.I.F.E.

If we are truly humble and broken,
If we have genuinely surrendered our lives to Christ,
If we have confessed the exact nature of our sins,
If we continue to grow in our relationship with the Lord,
If we desire to become people of purity and integrity,
If we continually seek to correct the sins of our past,
If we remain constantly in accountability with God and with others,
And if we search for ways to spread this message of hope,

Then we will experience these promises of transformation:

We will know that God loves us because He created us as His children,
    and sent His Son to die for our sins.
We will accept God's grace.
We will accept that there are others who love us regardless of who we are and
    what we have done.
We will stop equating our coping as love and nurturing.
Our lust will diminish.
Our fear of being discovered in our sin will stop.
Our fear regarding money will cease.
Our anxiety regarding the future will fade.
We will learn how to make healthy choices.
We will become more in touch with all of our feelings.
We will heal from the wounds of our past.
We will be more intimate with our spouses and friends.
We will be better parents, adult children, workers, and people.
We will come to know, trust, and praise the Lord in ever increasing and meaningful ways.

Is this an unbelievable hope? *We think not.*

Our lives are testimonies that God is working in us,
Sometimes quickly and sometimes slowly,
    always toward His greater glory.

The Nehemiah Principles listed below serves to remind participants to utilize the corresponding Nehemiah Principles detailed in the back of this workbook (beginning on page **175**) into the L.I.F.E. Recovery Group's weekly reading material.

Nehemiah: Transformation Principles

1. Accountability begins with humility.
2. Accountability depends on honest confession about your situation.
3. Accountability involves asking for help and stating your needs.
4. The journey of healing is never traveled alone. You will need the army around you.
5. The process of accountability assumes that the enemy wants to defeat us, especially when we start trying to do the right thing.
6. In the face of overwhelming damage and discouragement, rebuilding may be a matter of just getting started.
7. Being transformed requires getting the garbage out of your life.
8. Transformation begins at home.
9. Transformation requires preparing ahead of time for the attacks that will come.
10. Transformation means guarding the weakest places where you're most vulnerable.
11. Accountability is always with a group, not just with one person.
12. Our motivation for transformation should be selfless.
13. Transformation means building as well as defending.
14. Transformation means putting positive things into your life.
15. Transformation is an ongoing, lifelong process, but God provides sustaining energy.
16. When tempted, remain committed to transformation without wavering.
17. Transformation targets you for rumors and personal attacks.
18. Transformation results in a willingness to sacrifice even your own life.

PRINCIPLE ONE
Assignment One - Admitting Our True Condition

We admit that we have absolutely no control of our lives.
The sin of our addiction has become unmanageable.

Confronting Reality: I'm Shackled in My Own Prison

Congratulations! Despite long years of deceit, lies, denial, minimization, fears, shame, and manipulation, you have picked up this L.I.F.E. Recovery Guide or have come to a L.I.F.E. Recovery Group meeting. You have wanted to, thinking that perhaps you should, pondering if it was the right thing to do. You have resisted, found excuses, wondered who would find out, and worried about the consequences of getting honest. You've thought that no one would really understand. You've either believed that you have done the worst things possible – things no one else has ever done; or you've thought your stuff is not so bad - that you really don't need to come to a meeting and admit to others that you need help. Hear these words:

Welcome.
You're in the right place.
We're glad you're here.

That phrase, "the sin of my addiction," may stir some discomfort, if not down-right fear, for some. Addictive behavior is harmful to our physical body, mind, and spirit. During the time of "active addiction," we are living in rebellion to the will and plan of God, our Creator. In the Bible these acts of rebellion are called 'sin' and are revealed in our attitudes and behaviors that are against what God desires for us and from us. He created us to be His image incarnate, but rebellion entered into the Garden of Eden when our ancestors, Adam and Eve, disobeyed God by eating from the forbidden tree. Recognize that this act would not have taken place without there first being the attitude of rebellion against God and the decision made for the self to be in control; "to have it my way."

There are stories in the Bible called "parables," earthly stories with a "moral" and a spiritual meaning. Imagine what it was like for the Prodigal Son. He was much like us in that he wanted to be in control of his own life. So he asked for, and received, his inheritance to underwrite his move to the city to start life on his own. Off he goes to the big city and engages in (what the Bible calls) "riotous living." He lived it up until the great economic depression (the Bible calls it a famine) came along, and the next thing he knew he had used up his resources. And there was no one to help him. (Isn't that just like "friends"? While you have plenty they are with you, but where are they when you are in need?) So he took a job (as we call it) 'slopping the hogs.' (Ironic isn't it; he's not "living high off the hog" now, is he?) This was an insult to a Jewish boy. He did not even have sustenance as good as the hogs. He decided that since the servants of his father were living better than he, he would go home and hire on as a servant to his father. He has suffered abandonment, rejection, humiliation, failure, depression, and who knows what else, and now he will add embarrassment as he goes crawling home to his father begging for a job.

Does any of this look like or sound like your experience? It is at this point that many turn to addictions, suicide, or insanity to cope with the pain of their predicament. What choices have you made? Some turn to partying, but the parties lead to other behaviors that lead to further problems. Sooner or later, the party is over, then what? The Prodigal Son just wanted to be home. He didn't think he deserved to return to his earlier status as a son because his sins were so great. He hoped merely to be (like) one of his father's hired servants. Maybe you're like that; you're just glad to be alive and able to get to a meeting. You'd like to simply be quiet and belong.

The Prodigal Son's father, however, rushed out to meet him (and don't miss this fine point: The Bible says that while he [the son] was yet *a long way off* [get those words] his father saw him [the father was looking and longing for his 'lost son'] and was filled with compassion. The father *ran* in view of the village, and threw his arms around his neck and kissed him to accept him fully and prepared a great feast. That is our picture of God's response to us. He is expectantly watching for your return.

There is great rejoicing when we come to or come back to our Heavenly Father. We in L.I.F.E. Recovery want to be imitators of God, "just like little children." It may feel like you're a little boy, or girl, who has just come on the bus or into the lunchroom or onto the playground, and you may be expecting to be rejected or at least ignored. Instead, someone rushes over to greet you! All of us have been where you've been. We understand your pain and your fears. We're glad you've come. God prepares hospitality like a feast. We can't prepare a literal great feast, but we can go to coffee later.

Many of our stories are very much like that of the Prodigal Son, and yet each will be very different in detail according to the experiences of our life's journey. Our results will depend on our choice to either face or hide from our past, present, and *expected* future consequences of our dependencies. For some, the pain of our past is more than we are equipped to manage successfully, so we hide from the pain of life we experience in the present. Trauma is a term we apply to painful experiences that overwhelm our physical, mental/emotional, and spiritual resources. *Acute* trauma is brief, less than four weeks, and we are able to regain our physical, mental/emotional, and spiritual 'footing' and return to a healthy life-style within a brief period of time. When the traumatic event, or events, persists beyond four weeks, we begin our search for relief from sources outside of ourselves, resorting to illicit drugs, alcohol, food, gambling, relationships, sex, work, or some other activity in which we can "lose ourselves" and "avoid the pain of living."

Eventually we find ourselves trapped in routine behaviors that are no longer working for us. It is for such a person that L.I.F.E. Recovery was given its vision and mission; to develop resources that help you find peace, and assist you with regaining "your footing" so as to return "home" to healthy living; physically, mentally and emotionally, and, most of all, spiritually. *"What does it profit a man if he gains the whole world, but loses his own soul?"* (Matthew 16:26).

In a book entitled, *Ghosts from the Nursery*, the authors present extensive insight into the effects of early trauma experiences (physical, emotional, environmental) upon early development (the first 33 months – gestation to age 2) that have lifelong consequences, and to which we react (note that word as compared to "respond") without conscious awareness. Another purpose for the first assignment exercise is to *begin* processing the awareness of our root issues, family systems or family of origin work, to answer the question, "Why do I do the things I do?"

This impact on our present behaviors makes it necessary to take a deep look at your history and answer the question, "How did I get here?" If you were taking a long road trip and found yourself "lost," wouldn't it be prudent to first identify where you are and where you want to go, as well as how you got lost so you could plan an effective and efficient correction to your travel plans? We need to apply the same principle in planning our journey to healthier living.

We have to come to terms with the pain in our lives. We admit the pain to ourselves first, then admit our pain to God and then admit our pain to others. Sharing your pain with others is possibly the most difficult of all, but it is in safe relationships where we begin to heal and learn to speak the truth that our lives have become unmanageable.

Your first assignment is simply to get honest with yourself. We know that the greatest enemy of our being open and honest is silence; you have been deceived to think that silence has been your friend in the sense that your silence has enabled you to continue in your addiction to the behavioral choices that you have continually made to ease the pain of life. We also know how carefully you've guarded the secrets of your dependencies, habits, or behaviors. It's hard to imagine letting your secrets out. These were your comfort, safety, retreat and reward. There are thoughts in your mind telling you, "No! You can't talk about that. Someone will go running and screaming out of the room!" Or "You did what?" and turn away from you. We encourage you to confront those demons: those voices that have kept you shackled in your pain for too long.

We know your fears of shame and rejection because we are on a similar journey of learning to live in freedom every day. We want you to tell us how bad your pain and acting out got and what it was like to feel powerless over your life. Chances are that others in your group have done some of the same things, had some of the same feelings. There is nothing, certainly no behavior or habit, that separates you from the love of God. (See Romans 8:35) No matter what you've thought or what you've done, it's time to come home to the heavenly Father who loves you and is longing for your freedom; He is waiting for you. (John 8:36). *"If the Son makes you free, you shall be free indeed."* (Romans 8:2). *". . .the Spirit of life in Christ Jesus has made me free."*

The assignment that you are about to undertake will take great courage. It will seem to be a risk and a challenge. Don't turn back now. Keep putting one foot in front of the other and head for home. The freedom you will experience in being in real community is worth all it will take to get there. *"Being confident of this very thing, that He Who started a good work in you will carry it on to completion until the day of Christ Jesus."* (Philippians 1:6). Trust in Him to rush out to meet you and guide you when the going gets tough. He will provide for you, strengthen you, and welcome you home! He will work through your L.I.F.E. Recovery Group when and if you let Him. You need the group, and the group needs you. It is in the safety of a L.I.F.E. Recovery Group that you can find your voice and learn to speak truth without fear. Welcome, you're home!

Assignment One - Admitting Our True Condition

Thus the journey begins. Every journey has a beginning. This one starts with identifying the condition we find ourselves in, developing some insight as to how we got here, affirming our wish to leave while seeing hindrances to our ability to leave, and focusing on the destination we wish to achieve. As you work your way through the list patterns will likely emerge suggesting that these behaviors have more control over you than you have over them, and your life has become un-manageable.

On the next page unhealthy behaviors have been variously divided into categories and groups of categories. As you look at these, note the behaviors that you have struggled with and to what degree, even if you were only involved with a particular behavior once. Try to remember how many times you have done each of these. You may have to estimate. No one remembers, for example, how many times they have masturbated or how many times they've spent money compulsively. State how often this most recently took place (once a day or more, once a week, and so on). Remember, not all use is abuse and not all abuse is dependency; our motivation is key to freedom. *Are we in the behavior to change our mood, relieve stress or prove our value?*

Identify methods of coping to change mood, relieve stress or prove value.

	Began	*How Often*
Body Image		
Sports	_____	_____
Fitness	_____	_____
Plastic Surgery	_____	_____
Possessions		
Spending	_____	_____
Hoarding	_____	_____
Stealing	_____	_____
Performance – Workaholism		
Career	_____	_____
Talent	_____	_____
Ministry	_____	_____
Acts of Service	_____	_____
Entertainment		
Gaming	_____	_____
Gambling	_____	_____
Movies	_____	_____
Soaps	_____	_____
TV	_____	_____
Internet	_____	_____
Social websites, Facebook etc.	_____	_____
Novels (Romance or otherwise)	_____	_____
Drugs (Legal or Illegal)	_____	_____
Alcohol	_____	_____
Sex		
Fantasy	_____	_____
Romance Obsession (Emotional Affairs, Online Stalking via Facebook etc.)		
Exhibitionism / Voyeurism / Frotteurism (non-consensual rubbing)	_____	_____
Masturbation	_____	_____
Affairs, Prostitution, Strip Clubs	_____	_____
Pornography	_____	_____
Anonymous Sex (name of the sexual partner is not known)	_____	_____
Cyber Sex (Phone sex, Sexting, Virtual Sex-Digital/ Electronic Experience)	_____	_____
Gaming with Sexual or Violent Stimuli, Anime (see Gaming in Definitions)	_____	_____
Same Sex Attraction	_____	_____
Offending (Rape, Incest, Child Molestation)	_____	_____
Bestiality	_____	_____
Sexual Anorexia	_____	_____
Food	_____	_____
Anorexia Nervosa	_____	_____
Bulimia Nervosa	_____	_____
Binge Eating	_____	_____
Relationships		
Dating	_____	_____
Marriage	_____	_____
Children	_____	_____
Family	_____	_____
Friends	_____	_____

Journaling Exercise: Your Timeline History

The purpose of this exercise is to eventually identify core beliefs that have developed over your lifespan; these core beliefs are foundational to decision-making processes and perceptions of your life experience and the behaviors that you have engaged in when having to manage painful emotions. I would suggest the use of a loose-leaf binder so that your history can be edited as you research among family members the time frames for which you have no recall. This is merely a suggestion; use a resource that will create the greatest comfort and ease for you. Also, this is not an overnight or one-sitting experience. Pace yourself, and take your time. Let this experience 'unfold,' not 'blow up in your face.'

To begin, describe your earliest life experience. (Age, What happened? with whom?)

Identify feelings associated with this experience (both while in the experience and, in a separate paragraph or paragraphs, your current emotional state as you reflect on the experience about which you are writing).

What did you do about those feelings during this experience about which you are writing?

What do you want to do about those feelings right now?

Journal the next experience that you can recall, using the above format.

Continue building your timeline, as you are able. If this becomes overwhelming – STOP.

Discuss your experience with a counselor or with a trusted friend. This is not intended to be a re-traumatizing event.

Journaling Exercise: Your Consequences

When our attempts to fix our own problems our way begin to create problems of their own, we call these additional problems **negative consequences**. But sometimes we experience positive consequences from fixing our problems our own way, too. I invite you to be honest with yourself about the benefits of some of your negative behaviors; after all, the benefits were the 'rationale' you used to continue in these behaviors. Ultimately, you will need to say, "Goodbye" to these old coping behaviors. This, of course, will likely add yet another painful experience to your lifetime experiences. But just like the person who has surgery to remove a cancer, we understand that things sometimes get worse before they get better.

Positive benefits of negative behaviors:

Consider the following areas of your life:

Physical	Spiritual (your relationship with God)	Legal
Emotional (feelings)	Family	Financial
Mental (thinking)	Social	Vocational

Negative consequences of negative behaviors:

Consider the following areas of your life:

Physical	Spiritual (your relationship with God)	Legal
Emotional (feelings)	Family	Financial
Mental (thinking)	Social	Vocational

PRINCIPLE TWO
Assignment One – Exploring Our Reluctance

We believe in God, accept the grace offered through
His Son, Jesus Christ, and surrender our lives and
our wills to Him on a daily basis.

Finding the Solution: I Have Only One Option

In the book of John, chapter 5, there is a memorable and dramatic story of one of Jesus' healing miracles. As the account records, outside of Jerusalem is a pool called Bethesda, which was known as a place of healing. Occasionally an angel would come down and stir the water, and whoever got into the pool first was healed. One paralyzed man had been lying there for 38 years.

When Jesus came on the scene and saw this paralyzed, despairing man, the Great Physician asked an unusual question. Now think for a moment. If you were the one who encountered this paralyzed man, what would you say? Perhaps you would say something like, "That must be tough," or "How can I help you get into the pool?" You might be wondering about this man's condition.

Instead of one of those expected responses, Jesus asks a different question: *"Do you want to get well?"* To us, that sounds rather stupid. Why wouldn't a man who has been lying by a healing pool for 38 years want to get well?

But Jesus is the master psychologist. He knows what to ask to probe into the heart of our paralysis: **"Do you want to get well?"**

Assignment One – Exploring Our Reluctance

"Do you want to get well?"

It's a crucial question for those in recovery. Let's be honest. The Principles you are learning in this L.I.F.E. Recovery Guide aren't rocket science. The exercises and tasks aren't the least bit difficult to understand. Achieving sobriety and living in freedom everyday is a pretty simple concept intellectually speaking. So why is it so difficult to do?

Answering that question requires that you examine your heart. Sure, a part of you wants to be free of your sin. In some ways you want to be responsible and whole. At the very least you'd like to be released from your shame…But, do you *really* want to get well?

Journaling Exercise: Do You Want to Get Well?

> **Write any reasons you can think of why you shouldn't give up your addiction. (Don't be pious and say you can't think of any.) What factors have kept you from embracing recovery? What excuses have you made about how hard it is to find help?**

James, the brother of Christ, says that we can be guilty of being "double-minded." He writes, "Come near to God and he will come near to you. Wash your hands, you sinners, and purify your hearts, you double-minded" (James 4:8). There is a part of you that has wanted to get well, and a part of you that has not. Coping has been your most important need, and, as such, it's been an important "friend." It's been what you thought about in your loneliest and most stressful times. You wonder who and how you will be without your addiction. Your fantasies of "it will be better when..." brought you "comfort," or so you thought. It's hard to think about being without them.

You cannot hang on and let go at the same time. Well, anybody knows that, right? Then why do we try to do it? Double-mindedness is an attempt to have allegiance to two masters at the same time; however, you cannot serve both at the same time so you 'split your mind' and switch back and forth, between whichever master serves the moment.

Understand that you may have to grieve the loss of your addiction in order to get well.

Yes, your addictive thoughts and behaviors are sinful. That's true. But it's also true that you'll probably go through a grieving process as you take the journey of healing. It's a normal part of recovery. It's even necessary as you wrestle with surrender. God understands.

Luke 14: 25-33 talks about *"counting the cost."* That's an important exercise if you intend to be transformed. It's vital that you examine the depths of your heart--the reluctance as well as the willingness.

Let us first do a 'cost/benefit ratio analysis.' One of the first considerations when making a choice of any kind is "What has my coping method cost me?" Then, consider what it will cost you to surrender this behavior; and finally, what will be the benefit of living in freedom everyday vs. remaining in the addictive behavior that has been my "friend" and comforter?

Journaling Exercise: Counting the Cost

1. **List the 'costs' that you have experienced as the result of your choices. Refer to Assignment One as necessary regarding the consequences of your choice of activities to anesthetize those pains of life you identified in Assignment One.**

2. **List the 'costs' that will result if you surrender this (or these) behavior(s)?**
   What will it cost you to give up your addiction?

3. **List the benefit (or benefits) of surrendering the shackles that keep you bound in slavery to this (or these) behaviors? What will be the further cost to you if you hang on to your addiction?**

4. **Write a goodbye letter to your addiction(s) and let's get on with the business of getting well.**

Understand that you may have to grieve the loss of your addiction in order to get well. As with any grief experience, allow yourself time, be patient with yourself regarding your emotions and the resulting behaviors, and maintain open communication with your support system.

Even though your addictive thoughts and behavior are sinful, you'll probably go through a grieving process as you surrender these behaviors and begin the journey of healing. It's normal and even a necessary part of recovery. If you haven't already, now may be a good time to pause this assignment work and begin the deeper work in the L.I.F.E. Grieving Guide.

This brings us to the focal point of Principle Two. You are convinced that your sin matters to God, but does your pain matter, too? Can you trust God with your heart? Despite our claim to be a Christian, when we're totally honest, most of us don't fully trust God. Many of us hardly trust Him at all. You know that you *believe* in God. That's not the question. The problem isn't belief; it's *faith* in the trustworthiness of God.

Do you trust that God will be enough? That's the core question of Principle Two.

You may feel ashamed of this lack of faith in God. It may be one of your hidden secrets, along with the ones you admitted in your work of Principle One. You don't understand how you can distrust God because you've been involved with religious things most (or all) your life.

The answer probably lies in the explanation of spiritual abuse. [You may want to review this topic in *Healing the Wounds of Sexual Addiction* for a deeper explanation of what it means to have been spiritually abused.] Briefly, spiritual abuse occurs when someone uses the Bible more as a weapon than as a guide. It's when others attempt to motivate you into right actions by fear or shame, instead of by encouraging you into a loving relationship with God. Spiritual abuse also happens when you experience any other kind of abuse (physical, emotional, or sexual) at the hands of someone who is a spiritual figure in your life. Like other forms of abuse, spiritual abuse warps our view of God. We naturally form our view of God according to our experiences with our earthly parents, especially our fathers. If your dad was physically or sexually abusive, how can you believe God wants the best for you? If a spiritual authority figure was harsh and judgmental, how can you understand grace? How can you trust God to meet your needs and to love you unconditionally if you haven't known safe people who loved you, no matter what you did? Some of us have even been hurt by the church as knowledge of our addiction became public, and we may have even been turned away by the church; if not by formal dismissal, then by those who simply turned their backs, and will no longer associate with us.

Journaling Exercise: Examining Your View of God

> *Write a description of your view of God. What is God like in your mind? What are some words that describe Him? (If you would prefer, draw a picture of how you see God.) Remember, the way you write or how well you draw doesn't matter. Don't worry about grammar or artistic ability. What is important is that you clearly identify what you really believe about God.*

Most people who struggle with their addictive behavior feel terribly alone. Your own experience may be to feel isolated and desperately lonely. You feel alienated from God and others. Yes, the secret of your addictive behavior keeps you from real intimacy with others, but the issue likely goes far beyond your problem with addiction. Your history of feeling isolated and alone probably dates back long before you started acting out. It probably began in your family. It comes from the core wounds of abandonment. A thorough explanation of what it means to have been abandoned is found in primary sources like *Why You Love, Feel, and Act the Way You Do*, by Dr. Tim Clinton and Dr. Gary Sibcy or *Making Peace With Your Past Workbook* by Tim Sledge. I also give a brief description in this *L.I.F.E. Recovery Guide* in Assignment Three of Principle One. Review some of these materials if necessary.

For our purpose here, remember that we're abandoned when some of our fundamental needs for physical, emotional, sexual, or spiritual nurture aren't met by our caregivers. Similar to the discussion about spiritual abuse in the preceding paragraphs, if a key spiritual figure in your life wasn't available in some way (physically or emotionally), then you've suffered spiritual *abandonment*. Again, that experience will color your view of God. You'll have difficulty believing God is really concerned about you.

Journaling Exercise: Healing Your View of God

1. *List the people you feel abandoned you in some critical way. Describe the abandonment.*

2. *Find five Scriptures that describe God's care and concern for you. Write down the references. Read them daily for the next week.*

PRINCIPLE THREE
Assignment One – Admitting Our Darkness

*We make a list of our sins and weaknesses, and
confess those to a person of spiritual authority.*

Telling the Truth: I Must Leave the Darkness

Your earlier work in Principle One called for you to admit to yourself and your L.I.F.E. Recovery Group the truth about your sin of addiction coming with choices and behaviors not in the will of God that medicate the emotional pain of your history. In Principle Two you affirmed that God is trustworthy and faithful to transform your life, if you surrender to Him. Principle Three confronts your sinful nature, and eventually prompts you to confess your sins to others.

Working on Principle Three will be painful, just as it was painful to complete the exercises of Principle One. This kind of pain, actually, can be very helpful in the journey of transformation. *Confession to another human being* as well as to God reminds us of how far we are from God. The sting in our heart teaches us to turn to Him. Experiencing consequences forces us to let go of control. A tender conscience motivates us to refrain from causing more harm. Don't be afraid of the pain of these assignments, but instead, walk through it to the place of living in freedom everyday.

Principle Three challenges you to understand your dark side – your sinful nature. We are all sinners and fall short of the glory of God, according to Paul. We are inheritors of original sin: *the sin of pride* which tempts us to take control, rather than to be submitted to God's guidance and provision. Your addicted self – your sinful self – has pridefully and, perhaps at the core, fearfully tried to hide the truth about your life. You've believed that you are bad and worthless and that others wouldn't love you if they really knew you, especially if they knew how and why you've medicated. You've feared that if people knew your secrets, they would hate you and leave you. These descriptions illustrate a principle known as "**intimacy disorder,**" which will be discussed more toward the end of this assignment.

Assignment One – Admitting Our Darkness

LIES AND DECEIT: OUR WAY OF MANAGING OUR FEAR

Let's expand the concept of lying to any form of deceit, or being deceitful. Lying connotes speech alone. Whereas deceit includes lying, and enfolds manipulation, sneakiness, minimization, denial, and other strategies to hide the truth of our thoughts, feelings, and behaviors.

The result of your fear about your sins being discovered is that you've become a chronic liar, possibly even patho-logical in that you believe your lie to be the truth. You've sought to manipulate the opinion of others, because you've feared being caught and having to face the consequences. Perhaps you've arrogantly thought you could get away with your lies. Principle Three calls for you to courageously acknowledge the truth about your life, to yourself and to others.

Remember that we seek to admit our sinfulness not to increase our shame, but so that we can learn to depend more on God.

I hope you've already begun to tell the truth in your L.I.F.E. Recovery Group. I pray you've found it a safe place to share your reality and your pain. I trust you're getting some practice in exposing your darkness to the light. Allow God to illuminate the way as you work on these exercises.

Assignment One explores how you have lied to yourself and to others. Alcoholics Anonymous has many great slogans about recovery, two of which are applicable to our problem with lying. AA talks about an addict's "stinking thinking," and asserts "Your own best thinking is what got you here." Clinicians might say that we have "distorted cognitive thinking." Schools of counseling, both secular and Christian, sometimes approach our healing through attempting to change our thoughts. In Romans 12:2 Paul tells us to *be transformed by the renewing of your mind, that you may prove what is that good and acceptable and perfect will of God.* As Christians, we want to take every thought captive to Christ, including the "stinking thinking" of all the lies we have believed.

The first part of understanding the lies we've told to others is to understand the lies we have told *ourselves.* Lying is part of our original sin nature. When the serpent tempted Eve, he told the first lie, which was that she could eat the fruit of the forbidden tree and that she wouldn't die. Lying to ourselves often imitates that initial falsehood: We believe we can get away with something, and that we won't get hurt by our sin.

Have you told yourself these kinds of lies? That your coping or addictive behavior wouldn't hurt anyone else or even yourself? That you were different, the rules didn't apply to you, and that you could escape the consequences? This "stinking thinking" is a lot like eating too much food and believing we won't get fat, drinking too much alcohol and thinking we won't harm our bodies, or avoiding healthy habits and assuming we won't get sick.

Did you ever convince yourself that you wouldn't get caught? Did you think you were being careful and discreet? What precautions have you taken to hide your secrets? What manipulative behaviors have you used to avoid exposure?

Did you assure yourself that your sins weren't so bad; after all, everybody is doing it – aren't they? Have you justified a "lesser" sin because it prevented you from doing a more serious one? Like using alcohol instead of 'pot,' booze is legal, pot's not. Or used pot 'cause it's not as bad as the hard stuff like 'crack,' 'meth' or heroin. Or maybe you have just been chasing the big one at the lottery or the track. Then there is the most widespread addiction of all today, the result of which is epidemic in proportion – eating to calm boredom or anxiety. We could go on, but you get the point. Did you believe that you have the power to quit acting out if you really wanted to? Did you tell yourself that your sins weren't all that deadly? For example, have you ever thought that as long as your sins were never discovered, no one would get hurt?

Journaling Exercise: Your Lying

---

1. *What lies have you told yourself about your sins concerning your addictive behaviors?*

2. *Think back over your life. Do you remember the first lie you ever told to cover up sinful behavior? How old were you? Who did you lie to? Did you get away with it?*

3. *Think next about the first lie you told specifically to cover up your addictive behaviors.*
    a. *Again, how old were you? Describe the situation and your lies about it. Did you get caught?*

4. *If you can, trace the history of your deceitful behavior since that time. Make a list in your journal of all the major lies you've told.*

5. *What was your most recent lie? When? Who did you tell it to? Are you still keeping it a secret?*

Intimacy Disorder: Our Fear of Being Known

Patrick Carnes, a renowned addiction recovery expert states that, "more than 87 percent of patients come from disengaged families — a family environment in which family members are detached, uninvolved, or emotionally absent. All compulsive and addictive behaviors are signs of significant intimacy disorder and the inability to get needs met in healthy ways."

When we experience an intimacy disorder it is hardest to tell the truth to those whom we love the most. Another way of describing this phenomenon is that the person we are *most* afraid of losing will be the *hardest* one to let in on the truth.

You may be experiencing this dynamic in your group. It may have been relatively easy to come into your L.I.F.E. meeting and get honest. After all, the others are all in the same boat. They, too, are persons whose lives are (or were) out of control. You're reasonably certain you won't be judged too harshly, because the other group members have acted out in similar ways. And besides, the stakes aren't that high with your group. So what if they *do* think you're pretty awful? They're bound by a pledge of confidentiality and anonymity. They can't tell anyone else your secrets, and you can simply not return to the group. What have you lost?

You're finding it much more difficult; however, to tell the truth to somebody you really love. You may believe it's impossible to get totally honest with the most important people in your life. Your fear of being rejected if you're intimately known is keeping you in bondage and shame.

Journaling Exercise: Your Fears

Write the specific names of those people whom you are the most afraid of finding out the truth about your secret life behaviors [particularly your addictive behaviors] in which you have been engaging as a means of anesthetizing or 'managing' your emotional pain. Obviously, if you are married your spouse will probably be the first and most important person on this list. Next to each name, write the outcome that you most fear.

Name   *What You Are Most Afraid Of*

_____

_____

_____

_____

_____

How much have you been worrying about how others will react when they learn about your behaviors? Now, ask yourself if you're willing to go through life worrying about these kinds of consequences. Part of your process of transformation will be to build a character of honesty. You will no longer be comfortable living with your lies and deceptions. You will long for integrity. Start thinking about the courage it will take to get honest with the people whom you love the most.

**One of the great principles of becoming a person of wholeness and integrity
is accepting the risks involved in telling the truth.**

Journaling Exercise: Courage

Write a prayer asking for courage to tell the truth, even when you're afraid of the result. Ask God to help you trust Him with the outcome of this act of surrender.

Taking this kind of risk is one practical way we surrender our life to Christ. We clearly see that we can't control our own life. If we accept that God is in charge of our future, then what risks are we able to take? The reactions of others, including our spouse, are in the hands of God. Can you also surrender this outcome to Christ and dare to disclose the truth?

PRINCIPLE FOUR
Assignment One - Accepting Accountability

*We seek accountability and to build our character
as children of God.*

Growing in Transformation: I Mature in Character

Principle Four is about accountability and about character. In the early days of learning about accountability you may have many mistaken notions of what it means. As addicts, most of us resist the idea of being accountable. We don't like being told what to do. We bristle at the thought of having to check in with someone. When an accountability partner gives or withholds his permission for us to do certain things, we protest that we're being treated like a child. We question why we should submit to another person or allow someone else to control us so tightly.

(Now, be honest: Isn't your reaction fairly similar to what I just described?)

This independent, rebellious and prideful mindset is what makes most addicts resistant to the idea of accountability. It also represents many of the misconceptions about what it means to be accountable to someone for your recovery. A necessary part of healthy relationships is accountability to speak the truth. Accountability builds trust; trust builds healthy intimacy, that is, knowing one another. When the Bible speaks of "knowing," it is speaking of "experiencing" intimacy in the relationship. That word "intimacy," by the way, has nothing to do with 's-e-x' though sex may be involved. No, the intimacy of which I speak is openness, vulnerability. The word defines itself when it is broken down by syllables:

IN – TI – MA – CY

IN – TO – ME – SEE (say that real fast – intomesee)

In Genesis 2:2 we read, *"And they were both naked* ('nakedness' may refer to 'nudity,' but also means 'fully exposed'), *the man and his wife, and were not ashamed."* There was no sin at this moment in time; all was pure and undefiled; there was no shame (dismay, disillusionment or disappointment that things did not turn out as expected) until sin entered. After sin, there was shame and they tried to hide. Our attempts to cover shame is also insufficient, just like Adam and Eve who tried to *"hide themselves from the presence of the Lord God."* God then questions us too, asking *"Where are you?"* Not because God doesn't know where we are, but rather that *we* need to acknowledge the facts of *where we are,* hence our confession and accountability to God and to one another. Being honest with our confession/accountability with God and others is vital for *our* health and the health of our relationships. Accountability is our protection against sin, our addiction behaviors.

Assignment One - Accepting Accountability

Let's examine first your need for accountability. You may still believe that you can recover on your own or maybe by now you're convinced of the benefit of being in a L.I.F.E. Recovery Group, but that's as far as you want to go. I feel compelled to speak the truth to you in love: Remember it's your *own* "best thinking" that got you in this mess, right? You thought you could figure it out on your own, that you could avoid the consequences, or that the rules didn't apply to you. These might be some of the lies you have told yourself. Look back to the work you did on Principle Three - Assignment One.

Here's what God says: "Fools think they need no advice, but the wise listen to others" (Proverbs 12:15, *New Living Bible*). A beginning point of accepting accountability is to recognize our "foolish" status regarding our addictions or coping methods and our inability to change on our own. The wise person listens to the advice of godly group members who are further down the road in their journey of living in freedom every day; free from ineffective and harmful coping behaviors.

One helpful resource in changing your attitude is the book of Nehemiah, which gives a wonderful description of accountability. In the Appendix of this L.I.F.E. Recovery Guide you will find helpful details from the teachings from Nehemiah, and I suggest you read it as you work on Principle Four. The book covers a broad spectrum of principles that apply to the process of transformation, but it also contains a blueprint for accountability. The first principle outlined from Nehemiah is especially applicable here: *Accountability begins with humility*. Admit your pride and your powerlessness to achieve lasting change on your own, and take another huge step of surrender to God and accountability to the L.I.F.E. Recovery Group. Become teachable.

Next, challenge your negative mindset about accountability. I encourage you to view the concept as a vital tool of recovery, instead of some kind of negative force hovering over you. Like boundaries, accountability provides guidance and protection for your journey. An accountability partner is someone who watches your back, who stays with you on the wall (refer to Nehemiah for an explanation of that phrase), and who walks beside you to steady you if you begin to fall. You will soon come to see "boundaries" and "accountability" as friends, allies, and protection from the enemy we now know as our addiction.

This kind of **primary** accountability partner is called a **sponsor**, which is a term borrowed from the Twelve Step program of AA. This person is the *one main guide* who directs your program. Think of him or her as your coach.

It's important to point out that a primary mistake made by those in recovery is to have only one person as an accountability partner. You may have tried that approach, and it hasn't fully worked. As an addict, you're too smart, and too skillful at deceit to let only one person truly know you. It will take more than one or two people to keep you honest and directed in the early days of your recovery. That's why it's so critical that you participate in your L.I.F.E. Recovery Group and allow a *number* of others who fight the same or similar battles to know your heart. Your group becomes your team of support; the concept that allowed

Nehemiah to complete the wall (of defense) around the city of Jerusalem to protect against invasion from enemies all around.

But, as AA says, "First things first." In this initial assignment of Principle Four, you have one main job: To find a **sponsor.** Following are some descriptions of a sponsor to help you better understand what I mean.

Sponsors

> *And the things you have heard me say in the presence of many witnesses entrust*
> *to reliable men who will also be qualified to teach others. 2 Timothy 2:2 (NIV)*

These roles of a sponsor should be helpful in your recovery:

____A sponsor is someone who will hold you **accountable**. With this person you will be able to share all of your past sins, your acting out behaviors, your rituals, and your fantasies about how good your acting out behavior made you feel, and how the problems you were facing *seemed* to go away.

Your sponsor will help you develop a plan to manage crisis moments and resist the "craving" for the old ways of coping with the negative thoughts and feelings. If your sponsor sees you coming close to doing any of your rituals or acting out behaviors, they will, in love, directly confront you about them. We call this 'care-frontation.'

____A sponsor is someone who will give you **encouragement**. As you slowly make progress a sponsor will celebrate your success. Your sponsor is your biggest cheerleader.

____A sponsor is someone you can talk to and who will **listen**. Whenever you feel tempted, lonely, hurt, frightened, sad, or angry, you can call a sponsor to talk things over. Sometimes your sponsor will meet with you during such emergencies until the crisis passes.

____A sponsor is someone with whom you can **pray**. The two of you can seek the Lord's guidance together. You may also share Bible study.

____A sponsor is a **model**. Ideally, your sponsor should be someone who has had at least one year of sobriety from his or her addictions. Their success should serve as an inspiration to you.

____A sponsor is a **guide** who will teach you tools to use in recovery and show you the right path to being successful. Your sponsor will go over your L.I.F.E. Recovery Guide assignments with you as you do them. Your sponsor can direct your reading outside of the group, and may have ideas about therapy or spiritual direction. He or she is the general of your army.

These descriptions are clearly positive, aren't they? They're appealing, rather than threatening. I think we all have longed for this kind of person in our lives. We can become interested in (and even welcome) an accountability relationship with this kind of sponsor!

Who, then, can serve as your sponsor? *It* <u>*cannot*</u> *be your spouse, and it* <u>*cannot*</u> *be a member of the opposite sex.* A sponsor should be someone you can relate to, and preferably someone who is in recovery from the same form of addictive expression as you are working on (i.e.: alcohol or drug addicts with drug addicts – and in some cases the need will be to have a sponsor with the same drug experience; gamblers with gamblers; sex addicts with sex addicts, as with money, finances, and shopping or workaholics with workaholics, and similarly those with eating disorders), someone with more sobriety than yourself. The rationale here is that these persons are familiar with 'the games people play' with their deceitful hiding of their rituals and 'using' behaviors; it will be harder to 'run a scam.' Unfortunately in our addiction, we may try to seek 'sponsors' who will be more of an enabler by their ignorance; this is someone who will not be a good sponsor although they may be a nice friend. A good sponsor needs to 'know the enemy.'

Some suggestions include:

- a relative   someone in the church
- a friend   someone in your L.I.F.E. Recovery Group
- a pastor   someone with AA or NA or CA experience, or experience
                  with other faith based programs for recovery/transformation

The key to being a successful sponsor is having familiarity with the nature of expression of the sin that Satan continually attempts to resurrect in order to deceive, discourage and defeat your efforts toward transformation to living in freedom everyday.

It is understood that some groups may be so new that there won't be members with lengthy sobriety. Fortunately, sponsors don't always need to be recovering specifically from the same mode of expression of our addiction behaviors. Some L.I.F.E. Recovery Groups may need to rely on finding sponsors in other places in addition to the L.I.F.E. Recovery Group itself.

In many ways having a sponsor will be like having a surrogate parent. A sponsor must be tough, wise, and loving. If you were abandoned emotionally, physically, or spiritually by one of your parents, having a sponsor may seem very strange. Addicts, after all, are impaired in terms of intimate relationships. There may be times when you don't like your sponsor, and that's okay. He or she is like a signpost, showing you the way. There are times that I don't like the speed limit signs on the road when I am in a hurry. There will be times when you don't like what your sponsor is telling you. We love to isolate and not be responsible to or connect genuinely with anyone else. On the other hand, a sponsor may also be a wonderful presence in your life that you've never found before. In the surrogate parent role, a sponsor can help heal some of your wounds from the past.

So just exactly how do you interact with a sponsor? What specifically do you do together?

Concrete things you should do with your sponsor:

_____ **Call every day**. (Yes, every single day.) If you're not in the habit of talking with *your sponsor* every day, you won't pick up the phone to call when you're tempted to act out. Ask your sponsor to check on you if you fail to contact him daily. Perhaps you only make a brief check-in to report that you're sober today and doing okay. Other times you'll need to talk more extensively about some situation or struggle you're facing. *Just be sure to make daily contact with your sponsor.* Talking by phone is better than sending an email or texting. Remember we wrestle with an intimacy disorder, therefore you will have to be intentional.

_____ **Share with your sponsor how you're feeling.** During each daily phone call, text message, or email, report on what you're feeling. Identify if you're feeling glad, sad, mad, afraid, lonely, hurt, guilty, or ashamed. (You may be feeling one or all or some combination.) Filling in the blanks of this sentence also gives an opportunity to go deeper: I feel _____ about _____ because _____.

It's not your sponsor's job to fix your feelings, but it's good for you to get them out, and to be validated in your feelings; don't let anyone tell you, "You should not feel that way." Educate your sponsor on this issue, if necessary, by telling him or her that it would be more helpful for you if they were to ask , "What is making you feel the way you feel?"

_____ **State any temptations you've felt during the day**. Remember, bringing the secrets into the light removes their power. As AA says, "We're as sick as our secrets."

_____ **Confess** any boundary violations you've committed or slips you've had.

_____ **Ask for specific accountability** about an area or issue as needed, as an example, private time activities (remember, addicts love their privacy, their times of secrecy and isolation). Maybe you need to ask for accountability about where you go on your lunch break. You certainly need to be accountable about missing any L.I.F.E. Recovery Group meetings.

_____ **Process any circumstances or situations that are bothering you**. If you've had a fight with your wife or a friend, talk with your sponsor about what you could do differently next time. If you're frustrated with your boss, get your sponsor's input. *Talk about anything that is hindering your serenity.*

_____ **Work through these Principles of recovery**. Share your journal or notebook of the writing assignments in this L.I.F.E. Recovery Guide with your sponsor. Review especially your work in Principle Three – your "searching and fearless moral inventory." The best way to do this work with your sponsor is face to face, if possible.

_____ **Celebrate your progress in recovery.** Be accountable about your sobriety date and celebrate milestones such as one week, one month, three months, six months, and a year. Take your sponsor out to lunch or for coffee, and express your gratitude for the progress you're making with God's help and the help from him or her.

Summary of the Roles of Sponsor and Group Member

Useful in identifying, recruiting, and setting expectations with your sponsor

Sponsor Responsibilities	Group Member Responsibilities
Lovingly confront when needed, including (possibly) enforcing boundaries and consequences for group member (except in extenuating circumstances)	Submit to authority
Encourage the member with positive affirmations	Receive encouragement
Ensure group member submits a plan for his recovery and a contract about the sponsoring relationship	Prepare a plan of recovery and sign a contract with sponsor (see example)
Listen well: openly and non-judgmentally (don't try to fix)	Share openly and honestly
Be available to group member	Contact sponsor regularly and consistently
Pray with group member and teach to pray more deeply	Pray on the phone and in person with sponsor
Meet face-to-face with the member at least once a week and check the L.I.F.E. Recovery Guide assignments	Meet with the sponsor and share the L.I.F.E. Recovery Guide assignments
Call the member if he doesn't call by the appointed time	Call the sponsor by the appointed time mutually determined by the two of you
Strongly encourage the group member to enter individual counseling; assist with a list of recommended qualified counselors	Engage with a qualified counselor. If financial issues arise, seek financial assistance or programs that are underwritten.
Ask the group member to identify and discuss feelings	Openly and honestly identify and discuss feelings (use a feelings chart if necessary)
Ask group member to identify fantasy thoughts, cravings, or temptations	Communicate openly and honestly about fantasy thoughts, cravings, or temptations of the day
Monitor the group member's self-care in terms of rest, diet, exercise, and living a balanced life	Practice healthy self-care regarding rest, diet, exercise, and balance between family, work and play

A sponsor can't meet all your needs and won't be 100% available or perfect;

<u>Only God can be trusted to be totally dependable and perfect in every way.</u>

But a sponsor **is** a **vital** touchstone of your recovery program.

Journaling Exercise: Accepting Accountability

1. Is there anyone in your life right now who would be a candidate for a sponsor? <u>List the names of as many possibilities as you can think of</u>. Pray about each one and ask for God's guidance in your selection.

2. <u>Write down the date of your next L.I.F.E. Recovery Group meeting</u>. At that time, approach someone about being your sponsor. If you don't know anyone, your group may assign someone who has volunteered to be a temporary sponsor until you find a more permanent one. Don't worry about the temporary status. Just proceed in calling him/her every day until the next meeting and then try again.

3. <u>Write down the name of your sponsor</u>, whether he or she is temporary or a more permanent choice. If you haven't found one, note again the date of the next meeting and repeat the process of asking for a sponsor.

4. <u>Complete the Sponsor-Group Member Contract</u> (sample given) to formalize the commitments you and your sponsor are making.

5. <u>In your journal, keep a log of the times you've called your sponsor and the times you've met</u>. Keep it separately from your other work so you can access it easily. Refer to this record as a measurement of how well you're doing at staying connected. Report to your L.I.F.E. Recovery Group about your contact with your sponsor.

The next four pages contain a "Sponsor Contract," which you and your sponsor should complete. The contract also has some sample questions and other criteria to help both of you understand and remain accountable to these commitments.

SPONSOR – GROUP MEMBER CONTRACT

Member Name: _____

Phones: Home_____ Work_____ Cell _____

Sponsor Name: _____

Phones: IIome_____ Work_____ Cell _____

Group Facilitator Name: _____

Phones: Home_____ Work_____ Cell _____

Calling Schedule: _____ Sun _____ Mon _____ Tues
_____ Wed _____ Thurs _____ Fri _____ Sat

Format for Daily Contact: * Details follow for each item

- ✓ **Feelings Check** (core emotions, not just thoughts)

    I feel _____ about _____ because _____.
- ✓ **Get Current** (temptations, boundary violations, bothersome thoughts or situations, etc.)
- ✓ **Accountability** (Top Line and Bottom Line behaviors – see explanation)
- ✓ **Share Bible reading** (devotional or inspirational material)
- ✓ **Prayer**

Top Line Behaviors:

1. _____
2. _____
3. _____
4. _____
5. _____

Bottom Line Behaviors:

1. _____
2. _____
3. _____
4. _____
5. _____

Others in My Accountability Circle:

_____   _____

_____   _____

_____   _____

_____

Group Member's Signature and Date

_____

Sponsor's Signature and Date

Explanation of the Items that Make Up
Daily Contact with Sponsor

Feelings Check

There are only eight core feelings: **glad, sad, mad, lonely, hurt, fearful, guilty,** *and* **ashamed.** It's also possible to feel **numb,** which would be a ninth category.

Obviously, you'll experience gradations of these feelings, like *ecstatic* at just becoming engaged or *pleased* with the weather (both are variations of glad). You can be feeling *anxious* about an upcoming test or meeting or *terrified* because you've just been diagnosed with cancer (both are nuances of fear). Bottom line, though, all our emotions fall somewhere in one (or more) of these nine broad categories.

Often we share **thoughts** and describe them as **feelings.** For example, you might say, "I feel like you're not listening to me." That's a statement of opinion, **a thought** not a feeling. The feeling would be, "I feel *hurt* when you don't listen to me" or "I feel *lonely* in this relationship and *angry* when you don't stop watching TV to listen to me." See the difference?

Sponsor's Questions:
- *How are you feeling now?*   - *Have you had any other strong feelings today?*   - *What were they?*

When you communicate with your sponsor, include a "feelings check." Simply state your feeling(s) **in that moment.** If you had a different feeling(s) that dominated the day, share that, too.

Getting Current

To get current simply means to describe your day, including both the significant events and the bothersome ones. Getting current is providing a "laundry list" of what's happening in your life, especially anything that's eroding your serenity. It also includes disclosing any boundary violations you've committed.

Sponsor's Questions:
- *What happened today?*   - *Is anything bothering you?*   - *Did you violate any boundaries?*   - *What are you grateful for today?*

Accountability:

Remember, your sponsor is your main accountability partner. He/she is the primary person you invite to question you about your recovery program. Your accountability report should cover your *participation* in your "top line" behaviors (explained below) and your *avoidance* of your "bottom line" behaviors (also explained).

Defining Bottom Lines

Twelve Step groups often use the term "bottom line behaviors" to describe conduct you need to **avoid**, such as these examples:

- Controlling others
- Controlling self (in the sense of "white knuckling")
- Compulsively watching TV
- Compulsively shopping, cleaning or other secondary acting out behaviors
- Compulsively eating or gambling
- Compulsively working (to avoid relationships)
- 'Hanging out' with others who are engaged in addictive behaviors (drugs, alcohol, gambling, etc.) as this promotes an atmosphere of acceptance that places one at risk.

Defining Top Lines

"Top line behaviors" describe healthy choices you make daily, such as the following:

- Eating well
- Resting
- Playing well
- Praying
- Exercising/caring for your body
- Bible reading or meditating
- Connecting with safe people
- Journaling your activities, thoughts, and feelings
- Practicing gratitude

Sponsor's Questions about Accountability

Have you engaged in any 'medicating' behaviors today?

Have you fantasized or obsessed about your 'medicating' behavior of choice today?

Have you visited inappropriate places or people today?

('Inappropriate' defined as those places or persons whose presence would place you at risk)

Have you taken care of yourself physically, emotionally, mentally, spiritually, and socially today?

Are there any specific areas where you need to be accountable today?

Have you fully disclosed everything that you need to disclose?

Abstinence Period

These concepts about being accountable to a sponsor are tools to help you maintain sobriety. Hopefully, by this point in your progression through this L.I.F.E. Recovery Guide, you've achieved some length of sobriety from your addictive condition.

Obviously, sobriety begins when you stop medicating pain with the use of your coping method. At first glance, this "sobriety" definition seems straightforward. We addicts tend to justify whatever it is that we want to do, and we prefer to operate within a wide margin of behaviors we choose to view as not acting out. Being committed to a program of rigorous honesty (as well as being willing to go to any lengths to get well) demands we scrutinize all our actions.

A healthy recovery program with transformation as the goal requires a total, absolute abstinence period from all activity associated with acting out behaviors in which we were previously engaged in an effort to medicate our emotional pain, as well as intentional thoughts (fantasizing or obsessed "excessive, unreasonable zeal"). Abstinence could be for any period of time, but it is recommended to be at least 90 days. The purpose of this abstinence period is to help to "reset the brain chemistry" so that the person can begin to deal with life more realistically and rationally without medicating.

Neurochemical Benefits

An abstinence period serves several purposes and has a variety of benefits. First, by abstaining from escaping through preoccupied thoughts and their continued use, even in "tapering off," you'll experience a cleansing of your brain chemistry. As an example, an alcoholic or drug addict needs to be sober for a number of days before the chemical is completely out of their system, i.e. a time of detoxification, both physiologically and psychologically. We addicts have a constant supply of our "drug," because even fantasies (sexual and non-sexual) produce chemicals in the brain that cause us to feel pleasure. These chemical reactions are a natural part of life, but addicts have abused this and other chemical reactions to medicate and escape their feelings. Stopping your coping activities allows the brain chemistry to return to near normal; nevertheless, there may be lifelong residual physical consequences, especially for chronic or heavy users of chemical substances.

Another benefit of abstinence involves the addictive characteristic called tolerance. Tolerance means the addict requires more of the addictive agent to achieve the same result, and addicts find themselves continually "chasing the first high." An alcoholic or drug addict, for example, develops tolerance so that he requires more alcohol or drug to achieve the same effect, thus the same amount produces less effect. In similar fashion, behavioral addictions, such as gambling, sex, romance, shopping, work, and the like, build a tolerance for requiring more activity, or more exciting activity. You may find that you need a greater amount of stimuli than you once did, which has led you into more frequent activity and/or activity involving greater risk. Being abstinent for a period of time will help to reverse some of the symptoms from your acting out behavior.

Correction of False Core Beliefs

An additional reason addicts need to experience a fairly lengthy period of abstinence is for the purpose of changing their belief system. Addicts hold many (unconscious) core beliefs that have their roots in our life experiences. Most core beliefs are established before the age of five. (See "Ghosts from The Nursery" listed in the bibliography) Because we are all "needy" as a result of our abandonment trauma, our coping strategies soothed and satisfied us and we soon discovered our addiction was our most important need, for it was our best (though false) solution to the pain of our abandoned hearts. A period of abstinence exposes our core beliefs, which, for many, is the primary reason for the recommendation for individual counseling to identify and modify these unhealthy beliefs. This counseling is best engaged *after* the first 90 days of the abstinence period when the brain has had some time to 'recover' and thinking is more rational. Counseling may be very helpful to speed the process to gradually reverse the false belief system.

A period of abstinence will counteract another core belief: that our medicating is our most important need. (Again, our trauma of abuse and abandonment created this lie.) If you're married, to cite a sexual example, when you abstain from sex and still receive love from your spouse, you eventually learn a new definition of love. If you're single, through abstinence you'll discover that you can find love from intimate friendships that you couldn't find in acting out sexually or through unhealthy relationships.

Suggested Boundaries for the Abstinence Period

You should observe specific boundaries during a 90-day timeout period to help you abstain from coping strategies, acting out thoughts, feelings, and behaviors. Following are some suggestions:

- **Surrender credit cards; have no more than the minimum amount of cash on your person; establish an accountability record for *all* expenditures.**

- **Use no alcohol or drugs, other than those prescribed by your physician.** If you have *necessary medications*, discuss a plan with your physician, as well as your sponsor and accountability group, regarding the management and safekeeping of your medications. For many, legitimate medications become the *alternative* behavior of choice (switching addictions).

- **Watch no TV.** You may choose to make an exception for news shows, history, or sporting channels, or similar appropriate fare, but avoid soap operas, talk shows, sit-coms, and night-time dramas, many of which have alcohol, drug, and unhealthy relationship situations, which can provoke acting out thoughts, feelings, and behaviors, particularly in early stage recovery. Such programming encourages escaping into fantasy and can prompt triggers that you know are problematic.

- **Minimize fantasizing.** Many things can prompt a fantasy, but it's prudent to avoid those. As an example, music elicits powerful responses for many of us. If you're one who's strongly prompted by music, listen only to tapes or CD's, where you have control over what you hear. Review your list of acceptable music with your sponsor.

- **Change the routes you normally drive.** If certain roads are on the path to places that trigger for you (e.g. bars; homes of drinking and/or drugging buddies; stores, especially if there is a sales promotion; favorite restaurant, unless accompanied by someone with whom you have an accountability relationship; wherever you may be 'triggered'), then choose another way to go.

- **Establish a defensive protocol when alone at home for 2 hours or more**. Call your sponsor or an accountability partner before, during, or after extended periods of time alone in order to eliminate the "dead zones" of time when you're not accountable. Report what you'll be doing to stay out of trouble.

Withdrawal

Regardless of the nature of your addiction, there will be a period of withdrawal when you stop using your "drug of choice." All addicts similarly experience withdrawal symptoms when they stop acting out. Remember the neurochemical effects of compulsive behaviors that produce 'feel good' feelings? The brain reacts when there is no longer that influx of chemicals, and that reaction is called 'withdrawal' and may be noticeable.

Some symptoms of withdrawal include genuine physiological symptoms, such as headaches, body pains, sleeping and eating difficulties, or gastrointestinal distress. All are stress-related reactions that may come from stopping the 'medication' that you have been using. *If your physiological symptoms persist, or become an issue of concern, see your physician as soon as possible to rule out any serious condition and to provide treatment to prevent a serious condition from developing. Advise your physician of your withdrawal from the compulsive thinking, feeling, and acting out behaviors that have been your history.* Some will, also, experience psychological symptoms, such as anxiety and/or depression, which may be an underlying condition that is now made worse by your having stopped your "choice of medication." Other stress related symptoms may become apparent as time progresses; however, as you move further and further away from your experience of "using," these symptoms will diminish, if not be relieved all together. *If, after the 90 day abstinence period, you still experience emotional discomfort or distress, contact your physician who will evaluate and treat you as needed to bring relief. Be sure to advise your physician concerning your withdrawals from compulsive thoughts, feelings, and acting out behaviors.*

It's important to remember that "this, too, shall pass," as an AA slogan promises. You won't always feel so miserable physically **or emotionally**. When you sense that familiar craving to act out, remind yourself that it's temporary and it will pass. If necessary, this is a time to contact your sponsor because this craving places you at risk to act out. **Reach out for the "L.I.F.E. ring."** Compare the craving sensations to running up a steep hill. The feelings will intensify and resisting will get harder, but if you choose not to give up and give in, you'll soon be over the crest of the hill, and the going will be much easier.

PRINCIPLE FIVE
Assignment One: Assessing the Damage

We explore the damage we have done, accept responsibility, and make amends for our wrongs.

Demonstrating Real Change: I Accept Responsibility

Principle Five marks a turning point in your journey of transformation. Here's a review of your work to this point as guided by the first four Principles. In Principle One you have come to admit to the unmanageability of your life because of the sin of your acting out behaviors that have demonstrated your inability or unwillingness to trust God with your problems, and your inability to solve problems on your own using methods that have actually multiplied the problems. In Principle Two you chose to surrender your addiction totally to Christ, and to seek God's will for your life on a daily basis. Through your work in Principle Three you have inventoried your history with complete honesty, and through specific confession to God, to self, and to another person, you have revealed the truths you have discovered. In Principle Four, you have sought an accountability partner, as part of the accountability team, to address your flaws and inadequacies of character by entering into relationships of accountability as a matter of support and to maintain honesty with yourself.

These flaws and inadequacies stem from earlier woundedness and while learning to communicate these realities requires an expression of feelings and processing pain, these skills then develop into healthy interaction necessary for intimate relationships. These first four Principles are vitally foundational for genuine, lasting change. You have examined the depth of your sinful nature and your need for God, and you have taken the huge steps of telling the truth and asking for help.

Your journey thus far, though, has been largely self-focused. These examinations, confessions, and submission to accountability have required, and will continue to require, great introspection; you're looking inward and exploring your life, behavior, mind, and heart.

Principle Five expands your investigation. It will challenge you to look outside of yourself, and consider the ways your sin, your addictive acting out behaviors, has impacted others. You will continue to admit that you're not isolated in your sin, can*not* be isolated in your sin, and that it has repercussions for others. The effects of your addictive behaviors are like a pebble tossed into a pool of water: there are rings of ripples in the water that are ever multiplying, ever expanding; so with the expanding 'circles of influence' of our addictive acting out behaviors. The people known to you in your life, and people **not** known to you, are affected by your addictive acting out. Your actions have caused pain for many, probably more than you'd like to think. Your behavior and character flaws have harmed others in a variety of ways you have not considered. The process of Principle Five begins with a thorough assessment of the damage caused by your sin, its consequences, character flaws resulting from your woundedness, and the cause of your sinful behavior. Like Nehemiah, you will venture outside yourself to survey the damage that exists in your environment; you

will observe the fallout of your life; you will catalog the pain you've caused for others; and you will look unflinchingly at the harm you've brought about.

As in Principle One Assignment One, journaling your history, take your time with exploring the damage, and work at a safe pace for you; of course, by 'safe pace' we speak of emotional safety as well as physical safety. If the assignment becomes overwhelming – STOP, take a break. This is not a race to see how fast you can get through it. Discuss any struggles that are provoked either with your sponsor or counselor, or both. These ventures in discovery are not to be events that cause you to be re-traumatized.

Assignment One: Assessing the Damage

It may be helpful to think about categories of harm. Examples include relational harm (broken family relationships, broken colleague relationships, e.g. employment), physical harm, emotional harm, spiritual harm, and financial ruin; and you might come up with additional ways your sin has hurt others. Prayerfully ask God to show you the truth about your actions and the resulting effects on others.

Remember the reason for exploring the damage: *Its sole intent and purpose is **to reveal the hurt** so that you, and others, might become wholly healthy persons so that we may become holy persons. This exercise is* not *to increase your despair or add to your shame.* Be assured of this declaration of God's love for you, no matter what you've done:

> *"[The LORD] does not treat us as our sins deserve or repay us according to our iniquities. For as high as the heavens are above the earth, so great is his love for those who fear; as far as the east is from the west, so far has he removed our transgressions from us;" (Psalm 103: 10-12) and "Who shall separate us from the love of Christ? Shall tribulation, or distress, or persecution, or famine, or nakedness, or peril, or sword? . . . Yet in all these things we are more than conquerors through Him who loved us. For I am persuaded that neither death nor life, nor angels nor principalities nor powers, nor things present nor things to come, nor height nor depth, nor any other created thing, shall be able to separate us from the love of God which is in Christ Jesus our Lord." (Romans 8: 35, 37-39)*

That ought to be a booster shot to your confidence in Him to overcome!!

The purpose of Principle Five is to grow in maturity as you move away from any denial, blame, or self-pity and learn to accept responsibility for your actions. As you consider the many ways you've harmed others, you gain a deeper understanding of how your sins have hurt the heart of God. The Prodigal Son provides a perfect example of a sinner who was willing to take full responsibility for his behavior. He understood, too, how his sin had hurt his heavenly Father as well as his earthly one.

Before you begin the journaling assignments, read the story of the Prodigal Son in the Gospel of Luke, chapter 15, verses 11-20.

NOTE: Consider this assignment a *first step* in identifying those you've harmed. It's not something you can compile one time and be finished. As you grow in your transformation process, you'll identify others you will want add to the list. Don't be discouraged if this assignment seems overwhelming or never-ending. It's actually a sign of progress when you become aware of the broader or deeper layers of pain you have caused.

Journaling Exercise: Assessing the Damage

1. **Identify categories of people you have harmed.** Examples would include your current family (spouse and/or children), those in your family of origin, friends, coworkers, etc. Be sure to include those who've been indirectly harmed because of your addiction, such as spouses or children of acting out partners, or others who have looked up to you and been discouraged by your addictive behavior.

2. **List specifically all those you have damaged.** Write each name. Review the categories of people in your life as a guide to help you remember each person. Start with those closest to you, like your spouse and your children.

3. **Describe the nature of the damage next to each person's name.** Again, be specific. Some concrete examples might be:

   - Broke the marriage vows you made to your wife
   - Missed important events with your children because of your acting out
   - Spent money on acting out behaviors
   - Performed poorly at work
   - Acted hypocritically by violating your professed Christian standards

4. **After the description of the injury you've caused each one, list your character problem that fueled the behavior,** like your pride, selfishness, impatience, stubbornness, etc. (If you're not sure about the character defect, postpone this part of the assignment until you've completed Assignment Two of Principle Four, which deals with problems of character.)

Be sure to be gentle with yourself as you complete these lists. Maintain open communication with your accountability group and sponsor. Talk about your experience in this process with those in your L.I.F.E. Recovery Group. Seek encouragement from and give encouragement to your group members. Christ Jesus has paid the eternal penalty for your sin, and He will give to you grace in abundance to manage the temporal consequences that you will face in this process of wellness. Seek Him.

PRINCIPLE SIX
Assignment One - Practicing the Program

In fellowship with others we develop honest relationships, where we celebrate our progress and continue to address our weaknesses.

Living in Fellowship: I Cannot Succeed Alone

Congratulations for having come this far in your journey to maintain sobriety and wholesome integrity. It has taken courage, perseverance, and commitment. In many ways it may have been harder than you anticipated. Some may have considered giving up, but you have persevered, and here you are. You've experienced many feelings that have been painful for you: the old, familiar feelings which you have worked so hard in the past to escape. Now you are learning that, with the help of others of similar experience, you are able to work your way through the pain, stress and urgency without medicating. You may have experienced feelings new to you. You've humbled yourself in admitting the full truth about your history, your thoughts, feelings, and acting out behaviors. With God's help, you've made progress on a long journey. You've told the story of your road to addiction and the acting out behaviors in which you have engaged, and the life history that has generated the pain for which you have sought relief. You've decided that you want to get well and that the ways in which you have sought relief have not worked; and you have surrendered your life to Christ. You have begun to identify the wounds you have suffered that have been the source of your pain and the people who have inflicted these wounds, and have begun the process of forgiveness that will set you free from the bondage of your pain. Christ Jesus is the Power and the Strength that has gotten, and will continue to get you through. You've accepted accountability from a sponsor, and perhaps have begun working with a counselor. You have begun identifying those you have harmed by your behavior, and are willing to make amends to those you have harmed. I pray you're beginning to have a deeper sense of God's power and presence in your life.

Principle Six guides you into a way of living that involves genuine connection with others, instead of the isolation you've probably known. The foundation for this work comes from the following principle:

Fellowship is Equal to Freedom from Fear

It's probably hard for you to believe this promise since you may have been isolated for years as you've hidden your addiction from others, and have experienced the pain of relationships in which trust has not been present. You've never known the joy of a supportive community. Your shame has kept you from connecting with others, while it continued to fuel your craving for the acting out behavior of choice which produced the illusion of relief. (You also probably can't imagine a life free from your 'drug of choice,' the behaviors that produced the excitement of your addiction, which has felt like your constant companion for as long as you can remember.) Principle Six offers a path out of your isolation which, in turn, is the road to sobriety and wholesome integrity in a new lifestyle.

75

Hopefully, you're already enjoying some of the benefits of such fellowship through your L.I.F.E. Recovery Group. You're bonding with other Christians who have faced similar struggles and seek to live in sobriety and freedom. You're beginning to experience both the grace of God, and the grace from other Christians who will love you despite your mistakes.

Assignment One - Practicing the Program

Assignment One of Principle Six covers the basics of cementing this new way of life into daily practice. In this assignment we will be focusing on the *last* idea of the Principle itself: "We celebrate our progress and continue to address our weaknesses." I'll outline some specific, behavioral ways of walking the talk of transformation. **This assignment deals with the nuts and bolts of what the Twelve Step community calls "practicing the program."** Developing true fellowship with others must be built on this foundation.

I'm sure you've become convinced that recovery doesn't just happen. Unless you actually do things differently, your behavior and attitudes won't change. Two slogans from Twelve Step language describe this reality: *"If nothing changes, nothing changes;"* and *"If you keep doing what you've always done, you'll keep getting what you've always gotten."*
Assignment One details a variety of specific ways to do things differently. I've already mentioned them as part of different discussions from other Principles, but it's important to outline them clearly here. Think of this list as a "paint by numbers" plan of recovery. By this point you consistently should be:

- Caring for yourself physically (adequate exercise, rest, healthy diet, etc.)
- Attending L.I.F.E. Recovery Group meetings
- Calling someone from your group every day
- Reading this workbook and other helpful literature
- Enforcing healthy boundaries around your rituals and acting out behaviors
- Practicing honesty with yourself and others
- Taking responsibility for your actions
- Addressing your unhealthy attitudes and character defects
- Accepting accountability from your sponsor
- Participating in counseling treatment if necessary
- Asking God's help for your journey each day

Obviously, you won't be doing each of these things perfectly every day, but this list is a blueprint of goals for your daily life. How are you doing?

The next two pages contain worksheets you can use as a daily inventory to measure your progress. I suggest you make copies of these two pages and put them in your notebook or journal. Each day, evaluate yourself in the five areas described and record your "Inventory Score" as indicated on the chart.

Writing Exercise: Daily Inventory

Complete the Daily Inventory on the following pages and record your score on the chart. Remember, the first person to whom you are accountable is God and then yourself. Introspection can be difficult, but remember the desired outcome. Continue this practice each day for the next seven weeks.

Observe the pattern of your scores. Remember, the higher the score, the better. Look at each of the five categories as well as your total score. Are your numbers increasing or decreasing over the days and weeks? If your scores don't show progress, you may be in danger of reverting to old behaviors and attitudes. If that's the case, perhaps you need to revisit the earlier Principles. Share your measurements with your sponsor and L.I.F.E. Recovery Group each week.

DAILY INVENTORY OF HEALTHY LIVING

Evaluate yourself daily in these five core areas using the scale shown below. The items listed are just suggestions; add others that might be appropriate for you.

- Score each item in each area, and then *average* the total to reach an overall score for each area.
- Record those five scores on the Daily Inventory Chart (lower right box in the table).
- Transfer these scores to the Daily Inventory: Weekly Chart (on the next page).
- At the end of the week, transfer the daily average scores for the appropriate day to the day in the appropriate weekly column.
- Total the weekly scores and, hopefully, you will see your progress reflected in a rise in average scores.

Do not be discouraged for the dips in the averages as long as you see an overall steady improvement.

0	1	2	3	4	5
Doing poorly		*Doing somewhere in-between*			*Doing very well*

PHYSICAL AREA	**BEHAVIORAL AREA**
Nutritious eating	Sobriety
Adequate rest	Attending meetings
Exercise	Calling sponsor/Accountability team
Attending to medical needs	Healthy work habits
Recreation	Financially responsible

RELATIONAL AREA	**PERSONAL AREA**
Self-care (grooming)	Hobby/Recreation/Healthy leisure activity
Caring for possessions (living space, car)	Not switching to other addictions
Connecting with appropriate social contacts	Serene, instead of depressed or anxious
Considerate with spouse	Receiving counseling
Available to children	Healing from core wounds
Participating in supportive community (group, sponsor, other supportive persons)	Aware of feelings and needs
Helping others struggling with addiction	Reading recovery literature
Maintaining honest, healthy relationships	Able to express feelings and needs
Giving/receiving healthy compliments	
Giving employer the best 'product' you can	

SPIRITUAL AREA	**DAILY SCORE**
Prayer	**PHYSICAL AREA**
Bible study	**BEHAVIORAL AREA**
Personal devotional time	**RELATIONAL AREA**
Journaling	**PERSONAL AREA**
Corporate worship	**SPIRITUAL AREA**

DAILY INVENTORY CHART: WEEKLY

	SUN	MON	TUES	WED	THUR	FRI	SAT	TOTAL
Physical								
Behavioral								
Relational								
Personal								
Spiritual								
TOTAL								

[Total daily score will be between 0-25. Total weekly score will be between 0-175.]

DAILY INVENTORY CHART: SEVEN WEEKS

Assignment Level 1 _____   Assignment Level 2
Assignment Level 3 _____

	Week 1	Week 2	Week 3	Week 4	Week 5	Week 6	Week 7
Sunday							
Monday							
Tuesday							
Wednesday							
Thursday							
Friday							
Saturday							
WEEKLY TOTAL							

PRINCIPLE SEVEN
Assignment One - Telling Your Story

Having experienced healing from trauma, woundedness, and awakening in our spirit as the result of our work in transformation, we will strive to carry the message of Christ's healing power to those who still struggle, and we pursue a vision of God's purpose for our lives.

Finding a Purpose: I Have a Vision

Scripture reminds us *"where there is no vision, the people perish."* (Proverbs 29:18 KJV) This speaks for individuals as well as for nations. It is tragic the number of people who have no vision for their life, no purpose to fulfill, no thought for tomorrow and no hope for tomorrow. We are likely to ask, "Why on earth did I do everything I did?" "What was God's purpose for my life?" "How did I get so off track from God's purpose?" There are no easy answers to these questions but understand this:

You cannot undo what is done,
and
You must go forward from here.

As you work through our last principle you will learn how to go forward and use what you are doing now to carry the message of Christ's healing to those who still suffer. Just like in Luke 22:32 where Jesus speaks to Peter, *"When you have turned, strengthen your brother."*

In the first assignment you will prepare your story, which will become your testimony. You will begin sharing your testimony in the second assignment, first with your trusted L.I.F.E. Recovery Group, then, as you become stronger, with others. When you work on the third assignment you will be developing your Vision, your "Mission Statement" for how you want to conduct your life.

Developing your addiction story is foundational to determining what is next and answering the following questions: What will my life look like in the future? My dreams, desires, aspirations for the time that remains of my life? Answers to these three questions will unfold over the next 14 weeks in the form of your recovery story, where you started and where you will go all enveloped in the work to be done in Assignments Two and Three for Principle Seven.

Assignment One - Telling Your Story

The first time you attempt this assignment you should have at least six weeks of sobriety. If you haven't been able to manage this length of time without acting out, go back to Principle One and Principle Four and work on them again. Here's a review of several things you need to think about if you're struggling to maintain solid sobriety:

1. Are you willing? Do you really want to get well? Is there still a part of you that's resisting the hard work that you need to do?
2. Have you really surrendered your life to Christ? If you haven't, get with a pastor or some other spiritual figure and talk about what's holding you back.
3. Have you confessed your sins totally? Have you really made a complete list of all your addictive behaviors?
4. Have you truly put into place a comprehensive accountability group? Are you connecting with someone in the group on a daily basis?

Go over your answers with your L.I.F.E. Recovery Group or with several people who have long-term sobriety. Get some advice from your sponsor or from an AA sponsor as to what AA calls the "next right thing."

This assignment is straightforward, but it will take some time. To tell your story may sound like a simple assignment, but it's far from easy. Assignment One prepares you to tell your story in the most effective way. You've probably heard a variety of testimonies in your life, like at church or at a meeting. Have you realized the best ones are relatively short? It's a greater skill to be succinct, which requires really thinking about what you're trying to say. You've also surely read a number of articles throughout your life. Are you aware the typical magazine article is in the neighborhood of only 500-1000 words? It also takes great skill to write briefly and to summarize your themes clearly and concisely.

For your work here, decide how you feel most comfortable relating your story to others. There are two ways to share your story, and the one you pick depends on your gifts and abilities. Do you like talking or speaking, or do you like writing? Which method is most comfortable for you?

More important than the method you use is what you include in telling your story. The tradition in AA is to share your "experience, strength, and hope" by sharing three things: ***"what it was like; what happened; and what it's like now."*** This simple outline is a great way to organize your story. Following are some suggestions about how to flesh out your account. You should include several aspects in each of these main divisions.

1. **WHAT IT WAS LIKE**
   a. **Your addiction history.** You can include any elements of trauma that you experienced, but try to keep this portion brief and generally descriptive, not detailed. You're taking responsibility for your own reactions to your trauma, and not blaming others for the acting out behaviors that you've done. Be specific about your acting out history, but don't be detailed or graphic. You obviously can summarize some behaviors by describing categories of acting out, like escaping through fantasy, romance obsession, binging, anorexia, shopping, television, gaming, alcohol, illicit drugs, prescription drugs, gambling, etc. Be specific about things like how much time and money you spent on your unhealthy behaviors.

   b. **Your efforts to stop.** Describe your various attempts to stop acting out and make an assessment of why these efforts didn't work. Relate your emotional state during the frustrating times of not being able to find sobriety. Be honest about any level of spiritual or emotional immaturity that played a part in your failure to achieve sobriety.
   c. **Your consequences.** Outline the major consequences you experienced due to your addiction.

2. **WHAT HAPPENED**
   a. **Your "bottom."** When did you hit what AA calls your "bottom"? What happened that finally got your attention?
   b. **Your surrender.** Detail the day you really made a decision to surrender your life of sin and addiction. Go over any emotions and actions that were a part of this decision.
   c. **Your journey.** What has the journey of healing been like? What have been some of the significant moments?

3. **WHAT IT'S LIKE NOW**
   a. **Your current life.** Describe how your life is different today than when you were acting out. What has changed? What improvements do you see? What have you learned about God, yourself, and the fellowship of Christ and others?
   b. **Your gratitude.** Share your gratitude for God's grace, His transforming power, and what He's done, and is doing, in your life. Mention specifically the gifts you've found in recovery.

Journaling Exercise: Telling Your Story

Prepare either a ten-minute talk or a 500-1000 word article relating the story of your addiction and your journey in recovery. You can use any form of writing (long hand or computer) to write your story. You can prepare notes or an outline as if you were giving a talk, or you can actually record your story on audio or videotape as a way of practicing. You can also ask a safe friend to listen as you go over it.

When you've finished this preparation, report to your L.I.F.E. Recovery Group that you're ready to share your story the next time you cycle back to Principle 7.

PRINCIPLE ONE
Assignment Two - Understanding Our Cycle

We admit that we have absolutely no control of our lives.
The sin of our addiction has become unmanageable.

Confronting Reality: I'm Shackled in My Own Prison

Congratulations! Despite long years of deceit, lies, denial, minimization, fears, shame, and manipulation, you have picked up this L.I.F.E. Recovery Guide or have come to a L.I.F.E. Recovery Group meeting. You have wanted to, thinking that perhaps you should, pondering if it was the right thing to do. You have resisted, found excuses, wondered who would find out, and worried about the consequences of getting honest. You've thought that no one would really understand. You've either believed that you have done the worst things possible – things no one else has ever done; or you've thought your stuff is not so bad - that you really don't need to come to a meeting and admit to others that you need help. Hear these words:

Welcome.
You're in the right place.
We're glad you're here.

That phrase, "the sin of my addiction," may stir some discomfort, if not down-right fear, for some. Addictive behavior is harmful to our physical body, mind, and spirit. During the time of "active addiction," we are living in rebellion to the will and plan of God, our Creator. In the Bible these acts of rebellion are called 'sin' and are revealed in our attitudes and behaviors that are against what God desires for us and from us. He created us to be His image incarnate, but rebellion entered into the Garden of Eden when our ancestors, Adam and Eve, disobeyed God by eating from the forbidden tree. Recognize that this act would not have taken place without there first being the attitude of rebellion against God and the decision made for the self to be in control; "to have it my way."

There are stories in the Bible called "parables:" earthly stories with a "moral" and a spiritual meaning. Imagine what it was like for the Prodigal Son. He was much like us in that he wanted to be in control of his own life. So he asked for, and received, his inheritance to underwrite his move to the city to start life on his own. Off he goes to the big city and engages in (what the Bible calls) "riotous living." He lived it up until the great economic depression (the Bible calls it a famine) came along, and the next thing he knew he had used up his resources. And there was no one to help him. (Isn't that just like "friends;" while you have plenty they are with you, but where are they when you are in need?) So he took a job (as we call it) 'slopping the hogs.' (Ironic isn't it; he's not "living high off the hog" now, is he?) This was an insult to a Jewish boy. He did not even have sustenance as good as the hogs. He decided that since the servants of his father were living better than he, he would go home and hire on as a servant to his father. He has suffered abandonment, rejection, humiliation, failure, depression, and who knows what else, and now he will add embarrassment as he goes crawling home to his father begging for a job.

Does any of this look like or sound like your experience? It is at this point that many turn to addictions, suicide, or insanity to cope with the pain of their predicament. What choices have you made? Some turn to partying, but the parties lead to other behaviors that lead to further problems. Sooner or later, the party is over, then what? The Prodigal Son just wanted to be home. He didn't think he deserved to return to his earlier status as a son because his sins were so great. He hoped merely to be (like) one of his father's hired servants. Maybe you're like that; you're just glad to be alive and able to get to a meeting. You'd like to simply be quiet and belong.

The Prodigal Son's father, however, rushed out to meet him (and don't miss this fine point: The Bible says that while he {the son} was yet *a long way off* {get those words} his father saw him {the father was looking and longing for his 'lost son'} and was filled with compassion. The father *ran* in view of the village, and threw his arms around his neck and kissed him to accept him fully and prepared a great feast. That is our picture of God's response to us. He is expectantly watching for your return.

There is great rejoicing when we come to or come back to our Heavenly Father. We in L.I.F.E. Recovery want to be imitators of God, "just like little children." It may feel like you're a little boy, or girl, who has just come on the bus or into the lunchroom or onto the playground, and you may be expecting to be rejected or at least ignored. Instead, someone rushes over to greet you! All of us have been where you've been. We understand your pain and your fears. We're glad you've come. God prepares hospitality like a feast. We can't prepare a literal great feast, but we can go to coffee later.

Many of our stories are very much like that of the Prodigal Son, and yet each will be very different in detail according to the experiences of our life's journey. Our results will depend on our choice to either face or hide from our past, present, and *expected* future consequences of our dependencies. For some, the pain of our past is more than we are equipped to manage successfully, so we hide from the pain of life we experience in the present. Trauma is a term we apply to painful experiences that overwhelm our physical, mental/emotional, and spiritual resources. *Acute* trauma is brief, less than four weeks, and we are able to regain our physical, mental/emotional, and spiritual 'footing' and return to a healthy life-style within a brief period of time. When the traumatic event, or events, persists beyond four weeks, we begin our search for relief from sources outside of ourselves, resorting to illicit drugs, alcohol, gambling, relationships, sex, work, or some other activity in which we can "lose ourselves" and "avoid the pain of living."

Eventually we find ourselves trapped in routine behaviors that are no longer working for us. It is for such a person that L.I.F.E. Recovery was given its vision and mission; to develop resources that help you find peace, and assist you with regaining "your footing" so as to return "home" to healthy living; physically, mentally and emotionally, and, most of all, spiritually *("What does it profit a man if he gains the whole world, but loses his own soul?"* Matthew 16:26).

In a book entitled, *Ghosts from the Nursery*, the authors present extensive insight into the effects of early trauma experiences (physical, emotional, environmental) upon early development (the first 33 months – gestation to age 2) that have lifelong consequences, and to which we react (note that word as compared to "respond") without conscious awareness. Another purpose for the first assignment exercise is to *begin* processing the awareness of our root issues, family systems or family of origin work, to answer the question, "Why do I do the things I do?"

This impact on our present behaviors makes it necessary to take a deep look at your history and answer the question, "How did I get here?" If you were taking a long road trip and found yourself "lost," wouldn't it be prudent to first identify where you are and where you want to go, as well as how you got lost so you could plan an effective and efficient correction to your travel plans? We need to apply the same principle in planning our journey to healthier living.

We have to come to terms with the pain in our lives. We admit the pain to ourselves first, then admit our pain to God and then admit our pain to others. Sharing your pain with others is possibly the most difficult of all, but it is in safe relationships where we begin to heal and learn to speak the truth that our lives have become unmanageable.

Your first assignment is simply to get honest with yourself. We know that the greatest enemy of our being open and honest is silence; you have been deceived to think that silence has been your friend in the sense that your silence has enabled you to continue in your addiction to the behavioral choices that you have continually made to ease the pain of life. We also know how carefully you've guarded the secrets of your dependencies, habits, or behaviors. It's hard to imagine letting your secrets out. These were your comfort, safety, retreat and reward. There are thoughts in your mind telling you, "No! You can't talk about that. Someone will go running and screaming out of the room!" Or "You did what?" and turn away from you. We encourage you to confront those demons: those voices that have kept you shackled in your pain for too long.

We know your fears of shame and rejection because we are on a similar journey of learning to live in freedom every day. We want you to tell us how bad your pain and acting out got and what it was like to feel powerless over your life. Chances are that others in your group have done some of the same things, had some of the same feelings. There is nothing, certainly no behavior or habit, that separates you from the love of God. (See Romans 8:35) No matter what you've thought or what you've done, it's time to come home to the heavenly Father who loves you and is longing for your freedom; He is waiting for you. (John 8:36: *"If the Son makes you free, you shall be free indeed."* Romans 8:2: *". . .the Spirit of life in Christ Jesus has made me free. . ."*)

The assignment that you are about to undertake will take great courage. It will seem to be a risk and a challenge. Don't turn back now. Keep putting one foot in front of the other and head for home. The freedom you will experience in being in real community is worth all it will take to get there. ("Being confident of this very thing, that He Who started a good work in you will carry it on to completion until the day of Christ Jesus." Philippians 1:6) Trust in Him to rush out to meet you and guide you when the going gets tough. He will provide for you, strengthen you, and welcome you home! He will work through your L.I.F.E. Recovery Group when and if you let Him. You need the group, and the group needs you. It is in the safety of a L.I.F.E. Recovery Group that you can find your voice and learn to speak truth without fear. Welcome, you're home!

Assignment Two - Understanding Our Cycle

In this assignment you will keep looking at that silent self that has kept you in bondage. The purpose of this assignment is to continue to bring into the light that which has been cloaked in darkness. It is also to show you some things that you will need to work on in a very specific and practical way.

In his book *Out of the Shadows,* Dr. Patrick Carnes first described the predictable cycle that an addiction follows. Briefly outlined, it looks like this:

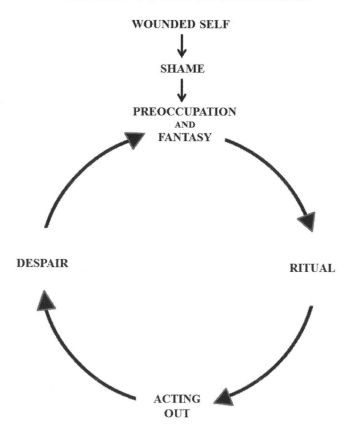

The cycle of addiction describes our phases or stages in a circular pattern that expresses the 'trap' in which we become entangled. Regardless of the nature of our addictive behavior of choice, the cycle remains the same. By this pattern we may be able to identify other behaviors that have taken control of our lives in this same fashion. Our goal is to break the cycle of addiction.   If we can successfully manage the first two stages we can break free before becoming entrapped. This is why counseling is so strongly recommended to help identify our woundedness and develop the skills to manage the thoughts and feelings that bring us pain and shame.

WOUNDED SELF is the term we apply to the result of a traumatic event or series of events; injuries that overwhelm our mental and emotional resources creating pain for which we seek relief.

SHAME is the root emotion resulting from the thoughts of the wounded self. These thoughts are triggered by the events experienced in life and are stored in our subconscious mind and are generally referred to as our core beliefs, out of which come beliefs about ourselves, our self-esteem, our value.

FANTASY is an attempt at trauma resolution, an escape from reality to provide a different outcome. Fantasy is defined as thoughts about the experience of using your 'coping mechanism' to change your mood or gain a sense of control and relief from your unpleasant emotional distress. We develop a dependency or affection for our behavior because of the relief (albeit temporary) that we feel. This has also been referred to as "preoccupation" – being preoccupied with the comforting thoughts and imagining the relief of your distress. The next assignment will help you understand more about your fantasies and what they mean.

Our thoughts lead to **RITUALS**, behaviors that we use to prepare to act out. Any thought or behavior that you use to get from fantasy to acting out is part of your ritual. Most of your work in this assignment is geared to help you identify your personal rituals. A ritual begins with **faulty thinking**, which launches the process long before you actually act out. The downward slide starts with the lies we tell ourselves. Your rituals will include thoughts of anticipation of relief, giving yourself permission to act out "just this once," that you can get away with it, and your plan to "set the stage" for your acting out behavior. Alcoholics Anonymous (AA) calls these kinds of thoughts "stinking thinking." They come in different variations at different times. The following descriptions will help you pinpoint your own thoughts that lead you astray.

What have you told yourself about why it is okay to act out? As a Christian you've had to get around the fact that you are disobeying God's plan for wholeness and health. Typically, we succumb to two main categories of stinking thinking:

JUSTIFICATION – For example, we might think that if we do enough good things for God, we are allowed to do a few bad things. It is as if we have a balance in our heads – a formula we have worked out – and we reason, "God won't mind if I do this, I've done so many other good things for Him." We may even believe our acting out is a way we can satisfy ourselves so that we can tolerate other things, like staying in a marriage, handling children, or our job or compensating for a lack of purpose in our lives. In our sick thinking, we see our coping as a positive benefit to just endure life.

ENTITLEMENT – Sometimes we justify our acting out by thinking that we deserve it, which is a form of "entitlement." Many of us have said to ourselves, "Nobody loves me and no one will take care of me. I have to do it for myself." We believe no one else understands us and the pain we feel. Down deep we're angry about not getting our needs met, and we feel entitled to meet our needs ourselves. Sometimes we really don't believe that God is good, that He will provide a satisfying life for us and meet our needs; so we use whatever has alleviated the pain and brought relief, thinking "Someone has to take care of this and it looks like it has to be me!"

Entitlement also tells us that we do so much, we have worked so hard, and we're so stressed that we deserve a reward. Because life is often so difficult, we might even think it's only fair to do these things. We deserve some comfort and gratification.

ACTING OUT is the result of preoccupation and ritualization to execute our acting out behavior. We have obtained the resources needed to carry out our intended behavior that we believe will bring relief to the pain or uncomfortable feeling that we are experiencing.

DESPAIR is feeling utter hopelessness and powerlessness about our behavior, and it follows our acting out as we 'sober up.' Feelings of shame, guilt, depression, and anxiety return this time triggered by our failure to maintain our sobriety. Addiction treatment identifies despair as an 'abstinence violation effect' which attempts to deny or cover up our acting out so that we then seek to gain a sense of control as we continue in the cycle of addiction. Addicts in despair are depressed for not living up to resolutions to stop and have increasing doubts that they will ever be able to stop which causes self-pity, self-hatred and sometimes thoughts of suicide.

Journaling Exercises: Your Stinking Thinking

Complete these following sentences in your journal:

My thoughts of justification include ….

My thoughts of entitlement include ….

In addition to our faulty thinking, **painful emotions** also fuel our acting out. They, too, can spiral us into our rituals. Remember, acting out is usually an expression of our **anger, anxiety, and depression**. We are lonely, yes, but it takes anger to get most of us past our moral and Christian beliefs.

Because of some of our painful experiences, both from our childhood, which we will explore in a later lesson, and from more current interactions, we addicts are often very angry, anxious, or depressed people. We are angry with those who failed to meet our needs and who hurt us. We are anxious or depressed because we are not able to control our circumstances. We are angry with those who have tried to confront us about our sins. And we use that emotion to sidestep our commitment to sobriety.

Journaling Exercise: Anger Inventory

Make a list of those people in your life toward whom you feel anger, anxiety, or depression. Next to each name, write down what makes you so angry, anxious, or depressed. Remember that you may also be angry with God, or anxious or depressed. King David, the "man after God's own heart," was furious with God at times, and he wrote many of the Psalms out of that anger. Job experienced depression when he lost his health, his wealth, and his family as God allowed Satan to test him to prove his faith. Elijah was both anxious and depressed as he sat under the juniper tree complaining to God about Jezebel's intent to kill him, and Joshua's anger and depression as he was sitting under the grape vine complaining to God because things did not go according to his desired plan. You also are probably angry with one other important person: *yourself.* You may be experiencing anxiety or depression because you have failed yourself, not measured up to your own expectations for yourself. Take as much time as you need to complete your list, and prayerfully ask God to help you. The following chart can serve as a guide.

Name	Reason(s)
_____	_____
_____	_____
_____	_____
_____	_____
_____	_____

As you go deeper into your recovery journey, we would like to suggest that you incorporate the use of the following statements to help work through the muddle that sometimes clouds our feelings and circumstances. Perhaps you might use this as an extension of the assignment above. Try to make a practice of using this framework every time you are attempting to express what you feel, whether in self-reflection, communicating with someone else, or with the Father.

Finish these sentences:

- "I feel _____ about _____ because _____."
- "I need _____."
- "My next action steps are _____."

The first sentence develops the "what" and the "why" that surround your feelings while the last two sentences guide toward better self-care and accountability. When contemplating what you need, instead of looking at behaviors to change or things you "should" do, try to look at universal needs such as, to be heard and understood, affirmed, blessed, safe, touched, chosen and included. Making this determination will help you express your need appropriately to God and others and by doing so you are taking responsibility for yourself. To help cultivate this as a habit, share this outline with your sponsor or accountability partners. This is also a great tool to help build your communication skills within your L.I.F.E. Recovery Group.

We have been looking at our stinking thinking (justification and entitlement) and our anger because they are the beginning points of our rituals. Once we have justified our sin somewhere in our mind, the next step is to prepare for acting out. These specific preparations are our rituals. It is important to identify our rituals, because stopping the ritual is key to stopping the acting out.

Following are some instructions to help you identify your rituals. You may want to make notes in your journal as you think through these questions. You may also need to talk to your sponsor or another member of your L.I.F.E. Recovery Group to get insight into your rituals. The best way to identify your ritual is to trace backward from your acting out behavior. First, select the sinful behavior that you have done the most. Now remember the last time you did that behavior. What happened before you acted out? Back up in time to the point you first started thinking about acting out in that way. From that thought, what did you do next? And then? Those actions are part of your ritual.

If, for example, you have used fantasy or romance obsession, start by thinking of the last time you indulged. Retrace your steps to the moment you first started thinking about this behavior, the "it'll be better when..." What were your thoughts at that time? How did you justify your behavior? Entitlement? Did you need to hide your using? How did you plan to act out? All of those things are part of your ritual.

Rituals may be short, like a single drink or 'hit,' or quite long, like a binge. Some rituals take weeks or months to develop. There are as many rituals as there are individuals and forms of acting out. Some may be unique to you. Others are nearly universal. Some rituals may be quite subtle.

Repeat this process of retracing your actions for any of your coping strategies. Start with the most common ones first and then progress to the ones that you may have only indulged in once.

Use the chart that follows as a guide to record your rituals. (To accommodate the next exercise, leave some space between each kind of acting out behavior).

Journaling Exercise: Your Rituals

Acting Out Behavior: **Ritual(s) Associated With It:**

_____   _____

_____   _____

_____   _____

_____   _____

_____   _____

Think and pray about how you were feeling going into your ritual. Were you lonely, stressed, frightened, angry, depressed or anxious? This may take some hard thought and conversation with other members of the group. Have you ever found that the excitement of just being in the ritual is enough to "medicate" the feeling? You may find that different kinds of acting out behaviors are associated with specific feelings. For example, you may find that feeling stressed or anxious leads you to acting out with substances while loneliness leads you into connecting with an affair partner.

Journaling Exercise: Feelings Behind Your Rituals

> *For every different kind of acting out behavior, write down (as best you can remember) how you were feeling when you started your ritual. Try using a different color to represent each emotion, like red for anger, blue for loneliness, black for depression, orange for anxiety, etc.*

BOUNDARIES: The Key to Interrupting Your Rituals

One of the great challenges of healing and building a new life is to intervene on these "preparations" – the rituals – you have used to escalate from preoccupation to acting out. It is one thing to say that you want to stop a particular sin; it is more complicated to stop your ritual behavior. It is almost impossible to stop the cycle at the acting out stage. You have to intervene *before* you ever get into your ritual. When you first notice that you have begun to fantasize, take action to interrupt! **A key principle to remember is that once your ritual has started, without intervention, you <u>will</u> act out eventually.**

It is imperative that you create a plan to stop the ritual behavior. You must conceptualize that plan very specifically. You must outline the **boundaries** you will need to keep you from entering into your ritual. These boundaries are the prohibitions which will keep you safe. They are the guardians of your sobriety.

Many addicts have come from a family setting that has failed to instill healthy boundaries. Family relationships exist on a continuum from detached to enmeshed; neither of these being healthy relationships. The following is to provide insight to healthy boundaries. Also, see Boundaries in the Definition section in this L.I.F.E. Recovery Guide.

Think back to a ritual that you described in the writing exercises. **What behaviors will you need to stop to avoid engaging in the ritual?** By identifying these behaviors, you can determine the boundaries you need.

For example, someone who uses alcohol will have to avoid the bars, liquor stores, and other outlets that market alcoholic beverages as well as neighborhoods and old friends who shared their drinking experience. Gamblers need to set boundaries to not engage in lottery or any other games of chance. This sounds harsh and very restrictive, but in the early days of establishing sobriety, it is necessary. Later stages of recovery will likely present less temptation because healthier means of coping will have been learned and put in place.

Journaling Exercise: Your Boundaries

For now, make a list of boundaries you'll need to put in place for each of your rituals.

Rituals: **Necessary boundaries:**

_____   _____

_____   _____

_____   _____

_____   _____

As I emphasized, rituals lead to **ACTING OUT**, which you've already identified in Assignment One. Are there any other forms of acting out you see you need to add to your list? If so, do that now.

The last stage in the cycle of addiction is **DESPAIR**. Another term for this desperate feeling is "depression." The vast majority of addicts are depressed; many of them also experience anxiety. Overwhelmed by guilt and shame, many addicts believe there is no other way to stop the pain.

Write about the most depressing time of your life. What was that like? What were the circumstances during that time? Have you ever thought about suicide? Have you ever acted on those thoughts? Are you feeling suicidal now?

Journaling Exercise: Your Despair

You may find that you need to be evaluated for clinical depression, which means that you see a professional to assess your level of despair. You might start with a counselor or therapist. If warranted, this clinician may refer you to a medical doctor, like a psychiatrist, who can map out a plan of treatment. (Some family practitioners, internists, or gynecologists will also address depression.) **If you feel suicidal at any time, it's vital you share those thoughts with a professional and get adequate help.**

ADDITIONAL WAYS OF ACTING OUT

Refer to the cycle of addiction diagram and note that the point of despair leads back into preoccupation and fantasy. Addicts seek to relieve their feelings of despair, often accompanied by feelings of guilt. They will believe, as crazy as it may seem, the best way to get relief is to start the process all over again. Addicts will return to the high of fantasy, and the cycle repeats.

For some, it's important to recognize that we also turn to other behaviors that "medicate" the feeling of despair. Roughly half of all alcoholics or chemically dependents are sex addicts. Many are smokers, hooked on caffeine, or on other "normal" drugs. Some turn to behaviors like work, sports, TV watching, or spending. We now know that many addicts have multiple addictions; i.e., they suffer from more than one addictive behavior. It's common for many alcoholics, for example, to discover after they have months or years of recovery that they are also sex addicts. In the journey of your healing, you may need to deal with other substances or behaviors that you use to alter your moods.

One of the ways I have looked at it was to remember how my family taught me how to avoid my feelings. We liked to watch TV, eat, smoke, play or watch sports, shop, work and go to church. My dad had scriptural answers for everything, and that isn't a bad thing, but it did serve to help us at times to avoid what we were really feeling. It may take weeks of sobriety to recognize some of these other behaviors.

Journaling Exercise: Your Additional Behaviors

> *Based on your awareness now, make a list of other addictions or ways you medicate the pain of your acting out.*

After all this hard work, take a grace break. Remember that we are all sinners and stuck in the cycle of our own sinful thinking and behavior. Even Paul admitted that he *didn't* do the good things he wanted to do, and he *did* do the things that he didn't want to. He said, "Oh, what a wretched man am I!"

Do you think God sent his Son to earth because we were perfect? God simply asks you to lean on Him more and more each day, and one day at a time, begin to understand how much he loves you. Remember again the story of the Prodigal Son and focus on how the father rushes out to meet his child. God is watching for you to come home and he is preparing for a feast.

L.I.F.E.'s GRIEVING GUIDE

Before you move on to Principle 2, Assignment 2, we'd like to give you an opportunity to address hindrances to your recovery plan; unresolved grief and pain. These negative emotions affect every recovery journey and they must be addressed for true healing. Now that you're sober, you most likely are feeling emotions that were suppressed by your coping. And now that you have practiced expressing your feelings in this assignment, you have the tools and ability to process the pain and losses that were a part of your past and addictive behaviors. We believe that now would be a good time to effectively work on the Grieving material included in the L.I.F.E. Grieving Guide. This Grieving Guide will help you identify and fully express areas that have been difficult to articulate especially while self-medicating. While this effort may take your lifetime to fully complete, the earlier you begin the sooner you'll be free from the burden that came with your woundings to live in freedom everyday. Once you've completed the Grieving Guide you will pick up where you left off on your Principle assignments.

PRINCIPLE TWO
Assignment Two - Surrendering Control

*We believe in God, accept the grace offered through
His Son, Jesus Christ, and surrender our lives and
our wills to Him on a daily basis.*

Finding the Solution: I Have Only One Option

In the book of John, chapter 5, there is a memorable and dramatic story of one of Jesus' healing miracles. As the account records, outside of Jerusalem is a pool called Bethesda, which was known as a place of healing. Occasionally an angel would come down and stir the water, and whoever got into the pool first was healed. One paralyzed man had been lying there for 38 years.

When Jesus came on the scene and saw this paralyzed, despairing man, the Great Physician asked an unusual question. Now think for a moment. If you were the one who encountered this paralyzed man, what would you say? Perhaps you would say something like, "That must be tough," or "How can I help you get into the pool?" You might be wondering about this man's condition.

Instead of one of those expected responses, Jesus asks a different question: *"Do you want to get well?"* To us, that sounds rather stupid. Why wouldn't a man who has been lying by a healing pool for 38 years want to get well?

But Jesus is the master psychologist. He knows what to ask to probe into the heart of our paralysis: **"Do you want to get well?"**

Assignment Two - Surrendering Control

A subtitle for Assignment Two could be "the choice I've never made." You may be feeling defensive after reading that heading. Maybe you bristle at the implication you haven't tried to do something about your addiction. You've probably done a lot of things about your addiction – except become sober from it. Addicts often surrender control to the enemy by giving up on any hope to change their behavior. You may have been there. But now, you are taking concrete, intentional steps toward living in freedom everyday! Therefore, you are to be commended on your efforts thus far to achieve victory, and strongly encouraged to keep on your journey, not only for sobriety, but to totally surrender to the Lordship of Jesus Christ Who is faithful to His promises.

Most of our past attempts to deal with our addiction were unsuccessful because they were more about our controlling our behavior instead of surrendering our entire life of real time moment-by-moment frustrations. We used a variety of excuses to rationalize this approach. (Review Assignment Two of Principle One, which outlines several examples of this kind of "stinking thinking.") We also excused half-hearted attempts to surrender with rationalizations like, "I don't want to make radical changes like ending a friendships. I can still be friends with those I have 'hung with' in the past and not have to participate in the acting out behaviors with them." Or if you are a workaholic you might have said, "I have to support my family. Am I supposed to quit my job?"

In more subtle ways we sometimes try to control or bargain with God about our addiction. We make attempts to stop acting out, and bargain that God will understand that this will take time. Or we may make deals with God: "If You, God, will do 'this' for me, then I will be able to give up this addiction." You might have assured yourself that you had 'sincerely' tried to surrender your habit to God when what you had really done was attempt to manipulate God into giving something that you deeply wanted.

Most of us have probably made many of these surrogate surrenders. We're usually quick to "surrender" when we're facing tough consequences of our addiction. We're afraid our partner is about to leave, our boss is about to fire us, or we'll be arrested for possession of illegal substance(s), so we promise to stop our acting out if God will only spare us the loss of our partner or family, or the pain of this legal fix you are in. Or we try to get by with a partial surrender. We give up an acting out behavior that we think is especially bad, but we hold on to other, supposedly less offensive, but no less problematic, behaviors. We stop using alcohol, or drugs, but we continue to engage in other behaviors that, while legal or socially acceptable, are no less an acting out to manage the overwhelming trial in our life. That approach is really only substituting one sin for another. That exchange hardly constitutes genuine surrender! Sometimes we may even stop acting out totally for a while (by "white knuckling"), but we don't truly surrender our hearts and wills to God.

Some of us have tried to manipulate and control others, especially our spouses, by pseudo efforts to surrender. We may agree to go to counseling as long as our spouse agrees to stop pestering us about it. But though we sit in a counselor's office for an hour a week, we never commit to a genuine process of change.

Occasionally, an addict will surrender the specifics of his addiction, but will continue to hold on to it in his heart. By that I mean that the now-sober addict will refuse to look any deeper than the sinful behaviors. If he's not physically acting out, he considers himself cured. He won't look at his character defects of pride or jealousy or insecurity or control. He's really nothing more than what AA calls a "dry drunk." Usually, he's still medicating with other more acceptable means like working or spending or losing himself in his children.

That kind of "surrender" falls far short of God's call. He challenges us to "offer your bodies as living sacrifices, holy and pleasing to God – this is your spiritual act of worship. Do not conform any longer to the pattern of this world, but be transformed by the renewing of your mind" (Romans 12:1-2). *God is much more concerned with our **transformation** than with our mere sobriety.* Can you honestly say you've truly surrendered to God in a spiritual sense? Are you willing to allow Him to transform you and mold you into the person He wants you to be? Do you ask Him to help you become that person?

A final example of a false kind of "choice" we make to surrender is our attempt to get sober on our own. Because of our shame and our fear of being known, we're tempted to try to recover without involving anyone else in our process. We believe we can recover in isolation by simply reading books, completing workbook exercises, or maybe talking with a therapist. But we won't share with others individually, and we sure won't go to a group where others are seeking to "get well."

This persistence of seeking recovery without becoming vulnerable to others exposes a key stronghold in many addicts' lives: the belief "I can do this on my own!" *We trust our ability to help ourselves more than we trust God.* We hope that if we just try long enough, hard enough, or "right" enough, we'll be successful. Instead of admitting powerlessness and surrendering totally to God, we try to work harder at getting it right by ourselves. Such efforts are doomed to fail. (I'll talk more in a later Principle about the pitfalls of refusing to be in accountability and fellowship with others.)

Journaling Exercise: Reviewing Your Choices

1. What are your excuses for not surrendering your addiction totally to God?

2. List some of the deals you've made with God about your acting out.

3. How have you tried to control or manipulate others by promising to get sober from your addiction?

4. In what practical ways have you declared, "I can do this by myself!" instead of relying on God. Describe any attempts you've made to achieve sobriety by yourself. Describe, too, the results.

5. Outline what it will look like to totally surrender control to Christ.

PRINCIPLE THREE
Assignment Two - Outlining Our Darkness

We make a list of our sins and weaknesses, and
confess those to a person of spiritual authority.

Telling the Truth: I Must Leave the Darkness

Your earlier work in Principle One called for you to admit to yourself and your L.I.F.E. Recovery Group the truth about your sin of addiction coming with choices and behaviors not in the will of God that medicate the emotional pain of your history. In Principle Two you affirmed that God is trustworthy and faithful to transform your life, if you surrender to Him. Principle Three confronts your sinful nature, and eventually prompts you to confess your sins to others.

Working on Principle Three will be painful, just as it was painful to complete the exercises of Principle One. This kind of pain, actually, can be very helpful in the journey of transformation. *Confession to another human being* as well as to God reminds us of how far we are from God. The sting in our heart teaches us to turn to Him. Experiencing consequences forces us to let go of control. A tender conscience motivates us to refrain from causing more harm. Don't be afraid of the pain of these assignments, but instead, walk through it to the place of living in freedom everyday.

Principle Three challenges you to understand your dark side – your sinful nature. We are all sinners and fall short of the glory of God, according to Paul. We are inheritors of original sin: *the sin of pride* which tempts us to take control, rather than to be submitted to God's guidance and provision. Your addicted self – your sinful self – has pridefully and, perhaps at the core, fearfully tried to hide the truth about your life. You've believed that you are bad and worthless and that others wouldn't love you if they really knew you, especially if they knew how and why you've medicated. You've feared that if people knew your secrets, they would hate you and leave you. These descriptions illustrate a principle known as "**intimacy disorder**," which will be discussed more toward the end of this assignment.

Assignment Two - Outlining Our Darkness

At this point in your recovery, you are waking up from the fog of your acting out behaviors. You're starting to get honest. Reality is sinking in, which might be frightening and discouraging. You probably were hoping for what AA calls, "a softer, gentler way." Be aware of your distorted thinking. Satan is likely telling you some lie like, "If this healing journey is so great, why do you feel so bad?"

Have you ever had an injury or some kind of surgery? You know that the recovery process is very often painful. You may feel a lot worse before you start feeling better. Healing from emotional trauma, sin, and addiction is no different.

Now, it's time to prepare an **honest inventory** of your life.

Be aware that you're in a process of grieving - grieving all the painful experiences of the past. You're dealing with your shame and asking, "How could I have done such terrible things?" These feelings are normal. Though painful, they actually are signs of your transformation.

The best way to counter the darkness of your past is to continue to expose it to the light. You've been hiding and denying your secret life for years, and your silence has made your life miserable. When Jesus confronted a man who had been possessed by demons, he asked, "What is your name?" The man said, "My name is Legion." It may seem that your sins are legion, and you may be overwhelmed by the enormity of your life's darkness. Nevertheless, it's time to complete what the AA program calls a "searching and fearless moral inventory," and expose that outline of sins to the healing power of God's grace.

Instructions about Your Inventory

In preparing this inventory or outline, it's perhaps easiest to divide your life into stages and categories. As you examine the various areas of sin in your life, remember the words of Paul concerning his sinful nature. He wrote about *not* doing the things he *wanted* to do, and about *doing* the things he *didn't* want to do. Paul is describing sins of *commission* and sins of *omission*. Think not only about the sins you've done, but also about the good that you haven't done. Include your actions or lack of actions, but also outline your negative or sinful thoughts and your lack of positive ones.

Divide your life into stages much like the way you created the timeline for your first assignment in this *L.I.F.E. Recovery Guide*. **One simple division would be these areas: childhood, adolescence, teenage, young adult, mid-life, and senior years**. (Obviously, some of you haven't reached all of these stages).

Next, think about categories of your life such as these: **family, education, social relationships, job or vocation, hobbies or recreation, sexuality, and your spiritual life**. Some of your work will duplicate the sexual and relationship history you prepared earlier. That's fine. *This inventory, though, will be much broader than just your addictive acting out behaviors. The intention is to outline every aspect of the sin in your life.* Explore every nook and cranny of your soul. Leave nothing hidden in the dark recesses of your spirit. The chart inserted below can be used to check the areas where you have completed your inventory work. The unmarked areas will be more visible to pick up where you left off.

Principle 3.2	Childhood	Teenage	Young Adult	Mid-Life	Senior
Family					
Education					
Social					
Job					
Recreation					
Sexuality					
Spirituality					

You may be overwhelmed by the variety or complexity of thoughts. Keep it simple. **Start journaling about one age and one category, and then move on to another**. Grow yourself up in your outline year by year, or at least stage by stage. Like all of the assignments in this workbook, this isn't a one-time exercise. It should be a living, changing document. You may update your inventory whenever a new memory or insight surfaces, even if that's years down the road.

Add examples (or even categories) as you think of them. You may have lied about many things or done a variety of crazy behaviors. You may have begun by sneaking or stealing cigarettes, or alcohol that you found in your home. Have you done anything similar? Did you ever cheat on a test or your income tax, take something that wasn't yours, or tell a lie to gain approval from others? **Whatever the sin, include it in your inventory.**

CAUTION

This is a long assignment, and you'll probably fill pages and pages of work. Don't worry about leaving things out. The first time you compile your inventory, you may only hit the high points (no pun intended). You can go back and get more detailed later. Remember that you're practicing getting honest and you're taking many risks. Recovery is a process.

As you work on this assignment, be sure to take frequent breaks. Talk to someone in recovery and get some support and encouragement. Be gentle with yourself. Remember again, *no sin can separate us from the love of God*. The sacrifice of Christ's blood cleanses us from all sin and makes us pure and holy in God's eyes. Allow His enduring love to comfort and sustain you as you humbly outline the failures of your life. God promises to transform you into the *"newness of life."*

> *Take note of this important boundary: This is not an exercise in which you describe in a grandiose way what a terrific sinner you are. This assignment isn't a competition to discover the most depraved person in the group. (The apostle Paul already claimed the title "chief of sinners.") Sometimes when an addict writes his inventory, it seems he's bragging about how terrible he was, so that his current state of sobriety will seem all the more amazing. False remorse is just another form of manipulation.*

Also, when you're sharing about your assignment in your L.I.F.E. Recovery Group, please heed an additional word of caution. Observe appropriate boundaries the way you did when you shared your acting out history. Don't be graphic in describing your behaviors, because you don't want to trigger (or educate) other members of the group.

Journaling Exercise: Your Inventory

This exercise isn't a simple 1-2-3 list like some of the assignments. Read the instructions and suggestions in the preceding paragraphs, and then begin outlining the sins in your life. Below are results from an Old and New Testament word study on "sin." Perhaps broadening the definition of "sin" might give insight for a more thorough inventory of your life.

Old Testament: Hebrew

- *Iniquity – perversity, depravity, twisting or perverting deliberately*

- *Transgression – rebellion against God and His laws*

- *Sin – offense, habitual sinfulness, youthful indiscretions, general state or specific occasion, particularly in reference to idolatry.*

New Testament: Greek

- *Sin – to miss the mark, to trespass, to err, to do an evil deed,*

Any way you organize your work is fine. The important thing is to write it down.

PRINCIPLE FOUR
Assignment Two – Assessing Our Character

We seek accountability and to build our character
as children of God.

Growing in Transformation: I Mature in Character

Principle Four is about accountability and about character. In the early days of learning about accountability you may have many mistaken notions of what it means. As addicts, most of us resist the idea of being accountable. We don't like being told what to do. We bristle at the thought of having to check in with someone. When an accountability partner gives or withholds his permission for us to do certain things, we protest that we're being treated like a child. We question why we should submit to another person or allow someone else to control us so tightly.

(Now, be honest: Isn't your reaction fairly similar to what I just described?)

This independent, rebellious and prideful mindset is what makes most addicts resistant to the idea of accountability. It also represents many of the misconceptions about what it means to be accountable to someone for your recovery. A necessary part of healthy relationships is accountability to speak the truth. Accountability builds trust; trust builds healthy intimacy, that is, knowing one another. When the Bible speaks of "knowing," it is speaking of "experiencing" intimacy in the relationship. That word "intimacy," by the way, has nothing to do with 's-e-x' though sex may be involved. No, the intimacy of which I speak is openness, vulnerability. The word defines itself when it is broken down by syllables:

IN – TI -- MA – CY
IN – TO – ME – SEE (say that real fast – intomesee)

In Genesis 2:2 we read, "And they were both *naked* ('nakedness' may refer to 'nudity,' but also means 'fully exposed'), the man and his wife, and *were not ashamed.*" There was no sin at this moment in time; all was pure and undefiled; there was no shame (dismay, disillusionment or disappointment that things did not turn out as expected) until sin entered. After sin, there was shame and they tried to hide. Our attempts to cover shame is also insufficient, just like Adam and Eve who tried to "hide themselves from the presence of the Lord God." God then questions us too, asking "Where are you?" Not because God doesn't know where we are, but rather that *we* need to acknowledge the facts of *where we are,* hence our confession and accountability to God and to one another. Being honest with our confession/accountability with God and others is vital for *our* health and the health of our relationships. Accountability is our protection against sin, our addiction behaviors.

Assignment Two – Assessing Our Character

People of integrity are people of character. Integrity and accountability are two aspects of character that we addressed in an earlier assignment. In this assignment we will examine other aspects of the Christian character that we are seeking to identify and develop.

Character refers to the kind of people we are even when there *isn't* accountability. Character is the way we live when we believe no one is watching or will find out. The apostle Paul, in Galatians chapter 5, describes a character marked by integrity. Integrity is defined as adherence to and remaining true to a code of moral values; it's when the Bible, your beliefs, and your behavior all line up. In this chapter Paul outlines the disposition of the sinful nature, and contrasts it with the makeup of a life lived in the Spirit:

> *The acts of the sinful nature are obvious: sexual immorality, impurity and debauchery; idolatry and witchcraft; hatred, discord, jealousy, fits of rage, selfish ambition, dissensions, factions and envy; drunkenness, orgies, and the like. I warn you, as I did before, that those who live like this will not inherit the kingdom of God. But the fruit of the Spirit is love, joy, peace, patience, kindness, goodness, faithfulness, gentleness and self-control. Against such things there is no law. Those who belong to Christ Jesus have crucified the sinful nature with its passions and desires. Since we live by the Spirit, let us keep in step with the Spirit. Let us not become conceited, provoking and envying each other.* Galatians 5:19-26 (NIV)

This is the theme of Principle Four. Working on the fruit of the Spirit will be a lifetime journey which in many churches is a process referred to as "sanctification." Perhaps this process won't be completed in this lifetime, but you can get started and stay engaged in the process.

The Angry (Wounded) Heart

Since anger, along with loneliness, is one of the main emotions that drive addiction, it's a good place to start. You'll notice how quickly Paul talks about anger in the passage above after he's described immorality, referred to in the Scripture verse as the 'sinful nature.' Paul uses a number of words to break down "anger": hatred, discord, jealousy, fits of rage, selfish ambition, dissensions, factions, and envy.

These words are all obviously different, but their root is the same: a wounded heart that's angry about not being loved and nurtured or able to control events that overwhelm our emotional resources. Realize that we all need to be affirmed, praised, heard, touched in healthy ways, adored, and included in a healthy community. When we don't feel we're getting these things, we can become angry like a little child who's having a temper tantrum. In fact, if you're like me, there's a lot about your acting out that was very juvenile, exactly like a temper tantrum. Anger, and a desperate need to get our needs met, will lead to our being ambitious, envious, jealous, and competitive. We'll have fits of rage, dissensions, and lots of discord.

Anger can come out in a lot of ways. Sometimes it's direct; at other times it's sarcastic (indirect). Some can be angry and not realize the anger that they are harboring. We might get angry at someone who doesn't deserve it (this is called 'projection') because whatever he or she said or did reminded us of an older wound and an older anger, perhaps even unconsciously.

It is important to identify what caused our original pain. Take a moment and ask God to teach you if your anger is older than the current situation. That is, if your anger at this person is really a reminder of an older wound. One way to identify older emotions is to ask, "How old am I feeling right now?" You may be surprised to discover you feel like you're very young. You feel small and vulnerable, and perhaps helpless. One symptom of responding in the moment to a much older situation is if painful memories come up for you. If you ask the right questions, memories of the original wound might surface. Don't be afraid of these memories. They're cleansing (when managed competently; for this reason we recommend being engaged with a professional counselor). We can't block out bad memories of old wounds, but with competent help we can resolve the emotional response. We learn to 'remember,' without 're-experiencing' the emotional content of these wounding events.

If you find that your anger is really out of control, you may need to work with a Christian therapist who can help discover its root. You may find that simply talking about your anger with trusted people will help dissipate it. Writing about the anger is another good way of expressing it. Remember, *anger can't be suppressed*; it will always come out sooner or later, usually in unhealthy ways; but we can learn healthy ways to *express* our anger and use that energy to resolve the problem(s) that provoke our anger. Anger is God-given as an alarm system that alerts us to the danger or threat to our being, real or perceived. We need to own our anger, seek God's help with identifying the threat, and "resolve the problem."

Often therapy and support revolves around understanding how we were wounded and feeling the freedom to express anger at those who wounded us. These steps are an important part of the journey. They allow us to know that we didn't deserve the things that happened to us. They are ways we grieve, and therefore, heal.

Journaling Exercise: Your Anger

> *For now, make a list of those whom you know you're angry with. Identify the people and write specifically what you're angry about. Share these memories with your group and ask them for feedback about any anger you might be showing today. Could it be related to these older situations?*

Our Anger at God

When you're exploring your anger toward others, don't forget about being angry toward God. In the pain of my addiction, I was often angry with God. Many times I had prayed for Him to remove my woundedness and the temptations from my life. I wanted to be magically healed or delivered. Even as a child I was angry that God didn't prevent me from all harm. Later, as I grew up, and even since I became a Christian, I could get angry with God about anything that didn't go right in my life.

And I stayed stuck in my anger with God. Of course, I didn't know it was okay to be angry with God. I thought my feelings were just one more item in a long list of strikes against me. I stuffed my anger deep inside my heart and never shared it with anyone.

Perhaps you've felt the same way. You've believed it was wrong to be angry with God. If so, get out your Bible and read some of the Psalms that describe how angry King David felt with God at times, or Job being angry with God for the unfairness of his trials. God doesn't ask us to squash our feelings, even the "bad" ones. Talk with God to discover His purpose for these events in your life and the resulting anger. He will tell you.

Journaling Exercise: Your Anger at God

Write a second list of reasons you've felt angry with God.

Now you have two lists of anger to share with your group. What do you do next?

I'm going to make a radical suggestion that might surprise you: **Decide to forgive every person on your list.** You might respond, "What? You just told me to be angry with these people, and now you're telling me to forgive them. I don't feel like doing that! Besides, none of them has asked for my forgiveness." This reaction is common, but it also springs from a misunderstanding about what forgiveness is.

Understanding Forgiveness

Forgiving someone else is for *your* emotional healing, not theirs. You can *decide* at some point to forgive even if you don't *feel* like it. Often, we get this order backward. We think we have to feel like doing something before we do it. Actually, the reverse sequence is true: Our feelings may *follow* our decisions; not the other way around. An AA slogan is, "Take the right action, and the feelings will follow." Regarding your need to forgive others, *forgiveness is an act of the will.* Healing emotions may follow immediately, or only after considerable time has passed.

Some of us have been counseled not to give up our anger too quickly because if we do, we'll stay vulnerable to being hurt again. Don't confuse forgiveness with your ongoing need to set healthy boundaries. You can be safe and still forgive. In fact, *forgiveness doesn't necessarily mean the reconciliation of relationship.* With God this is so, but in sin-sick human relationships it may not be healthy for you to continue in relationship with those who could cause you further harm. Your boundaries may need to include not having contact with those who hurt you, and that's okay.

Another mistake we make is in thinking that forgiveness is a one-time event. You may need to forgive someone over and over again whether from reoccurring memories or new injuries due to a lack of implementing boundaries. *"Then came Peter to Him, and said, 'Lord, how often shall my brother sin against me, and I forgive him? Till seven times?' Jesus said to him, 'I say not to you, until seven times, but until seventy times seven."* (Matthew 18:21-22) As was said earlier, our forgiving others is for our benefit too. In the simplest of terms, we let go of any sense of retribution to those who have wronged us or otherwise harmed us, in like manner as God has forgiven us by the atoning work of Christ for the wrong we have done against Him – doing so again and again.

Write in your journal about a specific decision you've made to forgive someone. Describe the offense or wound, then write a statement of forgiveness to the one who hurt you. You might begin, "I choose to forgive _____ for _____."

Journaling Exercise: Forgiving

Here's the bottom line: Forgiving someone is a *spiritual act of obedience*. It's what Jesus tells us to do: "Forgive us our debts (trespasses) as we forgive our debtors." Do you want to be forgiven for your sins? Practice forgiving others for whatever hurt they have caused you. When you've made a decision to forgive, then you must *act* like you have. Remember that you can still have your boundaries and you may still experience strong feelings, but you *act* in a way that brings honor to God by demonstrating to others His forgiveness extended to us. Refer back to the fruit of the Spirit that Paul talks about: love, peace, joy, patience, kindness, goodness, gentleness, goodness, faith, and self-control.

We can choose to act according to the fruit of the Spirit as an act of obedience to God, no matter how we feel.

With God, you, of course, don't need to forgive Him. But you do need to work on accepting that everything God has allowed to happen to you has been for a reason. Just because you don't understand the reason yet, doesn't mean there isn't one. Again, see the earlier discussion relating to the testing of Job. As I think back on all the things I was angry with God about, I see that from some of them, I learned some great lessons. Would I take that knowledge away? Not on your life! I've discovered that the times I'm most angry or disappointed with God have ultimately been the ones that are the most character-building. Growth is usually painful.

Reflect on what you have learned from the pain that God has allowed in your life. Write in your journal about some of those lessons if you can. There are a number of great books about this. One that has profoundly affected me is Larry Crabb's *Shattered Dreams*.

Journaling Exercise: Lessons Learned

> *Reflect in your journal about some of the lessons you've learned through adversity.*
>
> *How have these experiences built your character?*

Anger Fueled by Fear or Anxiety

Often, we are angry because we are *afraid*. We don't feel safe and we worry about the future. Our wounds from the past may have impaired our ability to feel safe. We've been hurt and abandoned, and we have memories of fear and anxiety. Something in the present can easily trigger us back to those older feelings. Fear and anxiety feed upon themselves and can create a vicious cycle of obsessive thinking about danger.

It's important to understand the difference between anxiety and fear. *Anxiety* is usually about something more global or general in nature – like being totally alone, having no meaning in your life, experiencing death, and being judged or condemned. *Fear* is usually about something more specific.

I am generally afraid of not getting my grass cut in the summer and my driveway shoveled in the winter (I live in Minnesota you understand). I can become really obsessed and worried about these things when they don't get done. I can get angry at myself for not doing them or at others (like my two sons) for not helping me. The fact is that taking care of my house symbolizes taking care of my life. A well cut lawn or a well shoveled driveway can help me feel that I am doing a good job of protecting my "space." It sounds silly, doesn't it?

Our "silly" obsessions are perhaps symbols of deep anxieties that we carry from our wounds. When you begin to understand that even little things can trigger you into deeper anxieties, you can realize why there are times when even little things bother you so much. An important part of assessing our character is understanding these "buttons" that trigger us into anger, anxiety, or fear. But how many of the things that you worry about have been labeled "silly" by others?

If you're really impaired by anxiety, the antidote may involve taking medication for a time. Don't be afraid of this approach; many people may need this help. Some of us have genetic predispositions in our neurochemistry to have more difficulty with fear and anxiety. Others have experienced such profound trauma that they need extra help to feel safe. Neither situation is something to be ashamed of. It's simply a part of who we are. Part of maturing in character may be challenging our pride or embarrassment at requiring this level of help.

Journaling Exercise: Your Fear

> *Write in your journal about the last time you felt really afraid. Can you identify any words or events that triggered the feeling?*

Fellowship: An Antidote to Fear

Another important antidote to fear and anxiety is the safety you're beginning to experience in your L.I.F.E. Recovery Group. We learn to be afraid in unhealthy relationships, and we can learn to feel safe in healthy ones. Assessing our character may involve recognizing how our trust of others is impaired because of our woundedness. Finding fellowship through a support group can be a huge step of faith.

During check-in time at every group be sure to report on any fears or anxieties you're having. Begin to think about what might help you to feel safe. At the appropriate times get some feedback from your accountability group about safety.

The main antidote to fear and anxiety is *developing a greater dependence on God.* The journey of transformation and recovery is a spiritual journey. As many times as necessary, refer back to the work that you need to do in Principle Two, and remind yourself of the ongoing discipline you'll need to grow in your relationship with Christ.

PRINCIPLE FIVE
Assignment Two - Planning Amends

We explore the damage we have done, accept responsibility, and make amends for our wrongs.

Demonstrating Real Change: I Accept Responsibility

Principle Five marks a turning point in your journey of transformation. Here's a review of your work to this point as guided by the first four Principles. In Principle One you have come to admit to the unmanageability of your life because of the sin of your acting out behaviors that have demonstrated your inability or unwillingness to trust God with your problems, and your inability to solve problems on your own using methods that have actually multiplied the problems. In Principle Two you chose to surrender your addiction totally to Christ, and to seek God's will for your life on a daily basis. Through your work in Principle Three you have inventoried your history with complete honesty, and through specific confession to God, to self, and to another person, you have revealed the truths you have discovered. In Principle Four, you have sought an accountability partner, as part of the accountability team, to address your flaws and inadequacies of character by entering into relationships of accountability as a matter of support and to maintain honesty with yourself.

These flaws and inadequacies stem from earlier woundedness and while learning to communicate these realities requires an expression of feelings and processing pain, these skills then develop into healthy interaction necessary for intimate relationships. These first four Principles are vitally foundational for genuine, lasting change. You have examined the depth of your sinful nature and your need for God, and you have taken the huge steps of telling the truth and asking for help.

Your journey thus far, though, has been largely self-focused. These examinations, confessions, and submission to accountability have required, and will continue to require, great introspection; you're looking inward and exploring your life, behavior, mind, and heart.

Principle Five expands your investigation. It will challenge you to look outside of yourself, and consider the ways your sin, your addictive acting out behaviors, has impacted others. You will continue to admit that you're not isolated in your sin, can*not* be isolated in your sin, and that it has repercussions for others. The effects of your addictive behaviors are like a pebble tossed into a pool of water: there are rings of ripples in the water that are ever multiplying, ever expanding; so with the expanding 'circles of influence' of our addictive acting out behaviors. The people known to you in your life, and people **not** known to you, are affected by your addictive acting out. Your actions have caused pain for many, probably more than you'd like to think. Your behavior and character flaws have harmed others in a variety of ways you have not considered. The process of Principle Five begins with a thorough assessment of the damage caused by your sin, its consequences, character flaws resulting from your woundedness, and the cause of your sinful behavior. Like Nehemiah, you will venture outside yourself to survey the damage that exists in your environment; you

will observe the fallout of your life; you will catalog the pain you've caused for others; and you will look unflinchingly at the harm you've brought about.

As in Principle One Assignment One, journaling your history, take your time with exploring the damage, and work at a safe pace for you; of course, by 'safe pace' we speak of emotional safety as well as physical safety. If the assignment becomes overwhelming – STOP, take a break. This is not a race to see how fast you can get through it. Discuss any struggles that are provoked either with your sponsor or counselor, or both. These ventures in discovery are not to be events that cause you to be re-traumatized.

Assignment Two - Planning Amends

Assessing the damage as a result of your addiction and listing those whom you've harmed is only the starting point. In fact, those acknowledgments are hollow if you stop there. The list you've created serves as the springboard into action – specific, identifiable action. Assignment Two of Principle Five prepares you for taking the actions of *restitution*.

First, I need to define what I mean by making restitution. The Twelve Step programs refer to these actions as "making amends for our wrongs." *In simple terms, making amends means offering an apology for the harm you've caused.* Its saying, "I'm sorry," with humility and without any expectation of receiving forgiveness. But making amends is also backing up the apology with specific attempts to make things right. Willingness to provide restitution is a good indicator of the genuineness of your apology.

Making Direct Amends

Addicts can offer two kinds of amends. The first is **direct amends**, where you provide restitution specifically to the person you've damaged. One by one, you approach the individuals who have suffered because of your sin, and you express your remorse for what you've done and for the pain it caused. If there is some overt way to right the wrong, you suggest it, and then provide it if you are allowed.

Zacchaeus, the tax collector mentioned in Luke 19, provides a great example of making amends through specific restitution. He had apparently used the authority of his position to collect more money than citizens owed. After his encounter with Jesus, Zacchaeus promised to pay people back four times the amount he had cheated from them. (See Luke 19: 1-9 for the biblical account of Zacchaeus' story).

Making Indirect Amends

A second type of amends is **vicarious restitution** (often called indirect amends). This approach is used when it's impossible or inappropriate to make direct amends. Perhaps you don't know how to contact someone you've harmed, or maybe the person has died. In some cases you may not even know the identity of those you've hurt, especially if your acting out has been extensive. These are situations where you can make vicarious amends. For example, you could donate funds to help the victims of DUI, or to help someone receive counseling or treatment for domestic violence (there is a high incidence rate of DV associated with drug and alcohol use as well as other addictive acting out behaviors). There are treatment agencies or other support services for recovering addicts that are opportunities for community service activities. Or you could make a personal contribution to L.I.F.E. Recovery, over and above the offering referred to in the L.I.F.E. Recovery Group meeting format. The possibilities of vicarious repayment are endless for the creative.

A second situation that warrants indirect restitution is if it would be harmful to make direct amends. You take this path when it would be more injurious to interact specifically with someone you've harmed. Certain domestic violence situations provide clear examples of cases where it's inappropriate to make direct amends. For instance, if there is a 'no contact injunction' in effect in a DV case, or other court action as the result of harm to family or other individuals that prohibits contact with any victim/defendant of your actions.

Explore Your Motives

Let me caution you about your work on this Principle. It's important you carefully examine your motive to make amends in each case. As addicts, we're used to manipulating outcomes, and it's possible you hope to benefit in some way by saying you're sorry. Maybe you think you'll be let off the hook or get back in someone's good graces. Those are flawed motives that will taint your actions and demonstrate a lack of genuine remorse for the harm caused. Refer again to the story of the Prodigal Son in Luke 15. He wasn't trying to regain his status as a son. In fact, he was willing to be a lowly servant to his father.

Here are some possible motivations that are self-serving: (inappropriate)

- to prevent or stop someone from being angry at you
- to make yourself feel better for what you've done
- to influence someone to trust you again
- to manipulate someone's pity or compassion
- to transfer blame by saying, "I'm sorry, but I wouldn't have done this if you hadn't done that"
- to attempt to avoid consequences by expressing regret

Here are some possible motivations that are focused on those who have been hurt by your behavior: (appropriate)

- to accept full responsibility for the harm you've caused
- to demonstrate empathy for those you've hurt
- to rectify your damage to the extent possible

Journaling Exercise: Your Motives

***Journal about your true motives for making amends in each case.
Pray for discernment and purity of heart.***

On the other hand, be optimistic and thankful for the changes God is prompting in you. As you've worked through these principles of wholeness and integrity, you've progressed from a place of denial to the point of being willing to accept full responsibility for what you've done and the harm you've caused. This difficult work in Principle Five is one more step in your transformation journey. Remember, God will be faithful to finish the good work He has started in your heart (Philippians 1:6).

Plan specifically how you'll go about making amends, both directly and vicariously. For each person, first determine if direct amends or indirect amends is most appropriate. Write the best method beside each name.

Journaling Exercise: Your Plan

Name of Person Harmed	*Kind of Amends (Direct or Indirect)*
_____	_____
_____	_____
_____	_____
_____	_____
_____	_____

Then develop a plan. Who will you approach first? How will you contact that person? What will you say? What action will you take?

Journaling Exercise: Who and How?

Identify the first three people to whom you can make direct amends: 1. _____ 2. _____ 3. _____ *Write your specific plan in your journal. Be as detailed as you can.*	*Then identify three ways of making indirect amends:* 1. _____ 2. _____ 3. _____ *Write your specific plan in your journal. Be as detailed as you can.*

Talk with your sponsor and L.I.F.E. Recovery Group about your list of those you've harmed, the damage you've done, and your plan for making amends. Ask for feedback. Are there any obvious omissions to your list? Are your motives as pure as you can make them? Is your plan appropriate and reasonable for the person and situation?

Journaling Exercise: An Appointment

Make an appointment to meet with your sponsor or determine when you'll share with your L.I.F.E. Recovery Group and record that time in your journal.

DO NOT TAKE ANY ACTION
without first sharing your plan with your accountability system.

PRINCIPLE SIX
Assignment Two - Changing Our Cycle

In fellowship with others we develop honest relationships, where we celebrate our progress and continue to address our weaknesses.

Living in Fellowship: I Cannot Succeed Alone

Congratulations for having come this far in your journey to maintain sobriety and wholesome integrity. It has taken courage, perseverance, and commitment. In many ways it may have been harder than you anticipated. Some may have considered giving up, but you have persevered, and here you are. You've experienced many feelings that have been painful for you: the old, familiar feelings which you have worked so hard in the past to escape. Now you are learning that, with the help of others of similar experience, you are able to work your way through the pain, stress and urgency without medicating. You may have experienced feelings new to you. You've humbled yourself in admitting the full truth about your history, your thoughts, feelings, and acting out behaviors. With God's help, you've made progress on a long journey. You've told the story of your road to addiction and the acting out behaviors in which you have engaged, and the life history that has generated the pain for which you have sought relief. You've decided that you want to get well and that the ways in which you have sought relief have not worked; and you have surrendered your life to Christ. You have begun to identify the wounds you have suffered that have been the source of your pain and the people who have inflicted these wounds, and have begun the process of forgiveness that will set you free from the bondage of your pain. Christ Jesus is the Power and the Strength that has gotten, and will continue to get you through. You've accepted accountability from a sponsor, and perhaps have begun working with a counselor. You have begun identifying those you have harmed by your behavior, and are willing to make amends to those you have harmed. I pray you're beginning to have a deeper sense of God's power and presence in your life.

Principle Six guides you into a way of living that involves genuine connection with others, instead of the isolation you've probably known. The foundation for this work comes from the following principle:

Fellowship is equal to freedom from fear.

It's probably hard for you to believe this promise since you may have been isolated for years as you've hidden your addiction from others, and have experienced the pain of relationships in which trust has not been present. You've never known the joy of a supportive community. Your shame has kept you from connecting with others, while it continued to fuel your craving for the acting out behavior of choice which produced the illusion of relief. (You also probably can't imagine a life free from your 'drug of choice,' the behaviors that produced the excitement of your addiction, which has felt like your constant companion for as long as you can remember.) Principle Six offers a path out of your isolation which, in turn, is the road to sobriety and wholesome integrity in a new lifestyle.

Hopefully, you're already enjoying some of the benefits of such fellowship through your L.I.F.E. Recovery Group. You're bonding with other Christians who have faced similar struggles and seek to live in sobriety and freedom. You're beginning to experience both the grace of God, and the grace from other Christians who will love you despite your mistakes.

Assignment Two - Changing Our Cycle

By now the cycle of addiction as described by Patrick Carnes is a familiar diagram. This graphic outlines the woundedness, which is at the core of our disease, the shame, our preoccupation and fantasy, our rituals, then our acting out, and of course, our despair. (Though I doubt I need to remind you about this cycle, you can refer to Assignment Two of Principle One for more details.)

I pray you're maintaining uninterrupted sobriety. I hope you're also experiencing some core changes of life and character. The journey you're making is about so much more than maintaining sobriety. **It's about the transformation of someone who is surrendered to Christ**.

Review the commission of Romans 12:

> *"Therefore, I urge you, brothers, in view of God's mercy, to offer your bodies as living sacrifices, holy and pleasing to God – this is your spiritual act of worship. Do not conform any longer to the pattern of this world, but be transformed by the renewing of your mind."* Romans 12: 1-2

God is after so much more than our sobriety. He longs to transform our sinful natures into a closer likeness of His Son. **He desires our heart**.

To illustrate this transformation process, I've created a cycle of recovery, which is diagrammed on the following page.

LAASER CYCLE OF RECOVERY

Instead of the addictive cycle of pain and sin, the transformed life of a new creature in Christ is characterized by this cycle of recovery. (We'll talk about vision in Assignment Three of Principle Seven.) Assignment Two, here, focuses on the main body of the cycle itself. It's actually just the visual representation of the behaviors I outlined in Assignment One. The checkpoints that make up the Daily Inventory are the Healthy Disciplines and Healthy Choices depicted in the cycle of recovery.

Review again the five core areas of healthy living that make up the Daily Inventory: physical, behavioral, personal, relational and spiritual. The items listed are examples of healthy disciplines, such as attending a L.I.F.E. Recovery Group meeting, calling your sponsor, or praying. These disciplines lead to healthy choices in behavior, thought, and character. Just like there's a predictable progression into sin, there's a known path of transformation. When you allow God to be in control of your life and heart, He can guide you into the pathway of joy as you grow in Him.

Being connected with the family of God provides the fellowship of healthy community. That's why I insist no one can ever recover alone. *God made us for relationship, which we obviously can't experience in isolation. We need each other.* It's partially through intimacy with others that we come to grow in intimacy with God.

When you live out the Principles of Living In Freedom Everyday, you invite others to be part of your journey of transformation, and you become part of theirs. You dare to admit your sins, ask for help, be accountable, accept responsibility, heal core wounds, and share the grace you've found in Christ. In healthy fellowship you find brothers and sisters in the family of God. You tell your secrets, expose your dark heart to the light and live in freedom every day.

Journaling Exercise: Expressing Our Gratitude

Write the names of three to four others who are part of your circle of fellowship. Write a sentence or two of gratitude for each one. Contact each person this week and share what you've written about your thankfulness for their part in your life.

Journaling Exercise: Changing Our Cycle

List the healthy disciplines you commit to focus on this week. Identify one from each core area you need to improve.

1. Physical	
2. Behavioral	
3. Relational	
4. Personal	
5. Spiritual	

Journaling Exercise: Reflecting On Our Changes

Reflect on the positive changes in your life over the last several weeks. Record three or four instances of joy that evidence your healthy choices.

PRINCIPLE SEVEN
Assignment Two - Sharing Your Pain

Having experienced healing from trauma, woundedness, and awakening in our spirit as the result of our work in transformation, we will strive to carry the message of Christ's healing power to those who still struggle, and we pursue a vision of God's purpose for our lives.

Finding a Purpose: I Have a Vision

Scripture reminds us *"where there is no vision, the people perish."* (Proverbs 29:18 KJV) This speaks for individuals as well as for nations. It is tragic the number of people who have no vision for their life, no purpose to fulfill, no thought for tomorrow, no hope for tomorrow. We are likely to ask, "Why on earth did I do everything I did?" "What was God's purpose for my life?" "How did I get so off track from God's purpose?" There are no easy answers to these questions but understand this:

You cannot undo what is done,
and
You must go forward from here.

As you work through our last principle you will learn how to go forward and use what you are doing now to carry the message of Christ's healing to those who still suffer. Just like in Luke 22:32 where Jesus speaks to Peter, *"When you have turned, strengthen your brother."*

In the first assignment you will prepare your story, which will become your testimony. You will begin sharing your testimony in the second assignment, first with your trusted L.I.F.E. Recovery Group, then, as you become stronger, with others. When you work on the third assignment you will be developing your Vision, your "Mission Statement" for how you want to conduct your life.

Developing your addiction story is foundational to determining what is next and answering the following questions: What will my life look like in the future? My dreams, desires, aspirations for the time that remains of my life? Answers to these three questions will unfold over the next 14 weeks in the form of your recovery story, where you started and where you will go all enveloped in the work to be done in Assignments Two and Three for Principle Seven.

Assignment Two - Sharing Your Pain

In Assignment One of Principle Seven, you made preparations to tell your story. Before you unleash yourself on others, take one more step. The goal of this assignment is to help you understand **what God has been trying to teach you about Himself through your story**. I'm not saying that God sat up in heaven one day and decided to make you an addict or even simply to permit all these crazy things to happen to you. God allows us to have free will and gives free will to those who wounded us. We gain knowledge of Him through our own decisions. Amazingly, God designed life in such a way that our experiences can teach us powerful lessons about what He is really like. Our job is to listen.

Many books can be resources to help with this assignment. I would encourage you to read Henry Nouwen's book, *The Return of the Prodigal Son*. (The biblical account is found in Luke 15:11-32, but you probably already know the story.) In powerful and insightful ways, Nouwen's book describes the roles of the Prodigal Son, the father and the older brother.

How is it, do you think, that the father in this story was so understanding of the son? How is this earthly father able to be so forgiving? Isn't he like most other earthly fathers, who would react more harshly to a disgraceful son? One interpretation is that perhaps this father had his own sinful past. Perhaps he knew what it was like to make mistakes and to feel like he was in the "pig pen." Did this father's understanding of how all of us turn away from home allow him to take his son back in such a loving and gracious way? Clearly, in this parable Jesus illustrates the forgiving nature of God.

What's equally obvious is your own status as a Prodigal Son. You acknowledged your sinful rebellion back in Principle One, and you've continued your journey of returning home – your path into L.I.F.E.

While the father was glad to welcome the prodigal home, not everyone had the same reaction. Do you remember the jealousy of the older brother when the wayward son returned? He was judgmental and angry. Does that reaction describe your attitude toward others still mired in the pig pen of sin? Do you at times feel superior because of your progress in turning your life around? Wouldn't you want to be like the gracious father and not the older brother? It's your own life experience that can teach you to be forgiving and encouraging to others.

I recommend another of Nouwen's books called *The Inner Voice of Love*. Nouwen personally experienced a time of great despair in his latter life. The word is that he struggled with some sexually sinful behavior. Eventually, he went on a personal retreat, where he kept a journal, just as you've been doing. Nouwen's journal was later published as *The Inner Voice of Love*.

One of his reflections in that book is very powerful. Nouwen says we should allow our pain to become "*the* pain." He believes that all of us have experienced circumstances in our lives that create painful memories and feelings. It is our pain. Nouwen goes on to say, however, that if we only spend time dwelling on the unique circumstances that caused our pain, we'll fall short of really understanding it. We might believe, he says, that if our circumstances had been different, we might not have any pain. Better, he thinks, is to come to an understanding that our personal pain is our "opportunity" to experience the pain of all humanity.

Think about it. What has connected you with others in your life? Was it success? Have your various achievements really brought you the peace and serenity you've longed for? Have you felt connected by being on the winning team? Or, have you felt more connected by getting honest in the last weeks with others who know what you've gone through? It seems to me that when we allow ourselves to share our suffering, we find true connection with other sufferers.

Another book with a similar message is Larry Crabb's, *Shattered Dreams*. He describes our reactions when we become shattered by life experiences and how we come to true connection through our brokenness.

Consider these words of Jesus:
> *"Come to me, all you who are weary and burdened, and I will give you rest. Take my yoke upon you and learn from me, for I am gentle and humble in heart, and you will find rest for your souls. For my yoke is easy and my burden is light."*
> Matthew 11:28-30 (NIV)

As someone who has struggled with an addiction, or many coping behaviors, you have lived that first part about being tired and stressed out. You have sought the rest that Jesus promises. But if you're like me, you've had difficulty understanding the last part about taking on Christ's yoke. Was His burden really light? It certainly doesn't seem "light" to me. However, when we understand the parable properly we will experience the "lightening" of the load, the burden, we bear. The analogy comes from agriculture where the yoke is the 'equipment' to place around the neck and shoulders of two oxen to carry or pull, a heavy load. When the two are working together, the load is lighter for each one. Another application in the use of the yoke is to train an inexperienced ox with an experienced ox to learn how to work while in the yoke with another ox. To lag behind brings pain; to go ahead will also cause pain. When we get in the yoke with Christ and follow His lead, neither lagging behind nor running ahead of Him, we are then able to manage the load together.

As God's son, Jesus gave up His status and became a man. As a human, Christ experienced the difficult things that we do. He was even afraid of the pain of his death and asked God, "If it be Your will, take this cup from me." Jesus felt abandoned in the Garden by His disciples. He was rejected and despised by His own people. He was tortured and put to a painful death. On the cross, He doubted and wondered where God had gone, until Jesus cried in despair, *"Why have You forsaken me?"*

When we're in relationship with Christ, we have a brother who knows how we feel. Do you remember what it was like to go to your first meeting, tell your story, and experience the huge relief that others understood? **You felt accepted; no longer abandoned.** In that moment, did your burden feel lighter? That is what Jesus is asking us to do — join Him in His yoke and experience the relief of the weight of our burden as we experience his strength to help us. It is in this way that our pain also becomes His pain. He shares our pain, our burden, and knows full well how it feels. After you've considered how your pain connects you with the pain of others, would you take away your past if you could? Do you see that perhaps it's allowed you to experience the pain of others who suffer? Your own pain has given you compassion and empathy for your spouse, your children, your brothers and sisters, and others whom you have hurt by your acting out. Can you begin to believe that the pain of your "burden" has been a gift? How else would you begin to understand the gift of God's grace through His Son Jesus Christ?

Perhaps, it's time to stop feeling sorry for yourself. Do you see why some introduce themselves by saying, "Hi, my name is _____, and I'm a *grateful* recovering addict"? That statement is a testimony to the transforming power of God!

Journaling Exercise: Depending on God

> ***Reflect and write in your journal about what your losses and pain have taught you about depending on God.***

Now, as you consider sharing your story, I ask you to reflect on any testimonies you've heard. Which ones have really been helpful and inspirational? Has it been those in which people bragged about how well they're doing, or has it been those in which people honestly and transparently told about their struggles and their pain? Perhaps it was the one who was willing to tell you their story that got you to come to a L.I.F.E. Recovery Group meeting in the first place.

Would you like to give the gift of your story to someone else? Remember back to all those times when you longed to know that someone else understood what you were going through. By God's grace, someone came along, shared their story of brokenness and healing, and now you're on the road to recovery, too. Right now, I'd bet that you know someone who needs to hear *your* story.

Consider people to whom you'd like to tell your story. They don't have to be possible or probable addicts. They just need to be people whom you know struggle. You may feel frightened at the idea of telling your story to "normal" (non-addicted) people. You may even be having a "shame attack" that is, you're thinking, "It'll be hard enough to tell my story to other addicts. How could I tell it to just *anyone*?" Relax for now. You'll probably begin sharing your story only with those you know are relatively safe. As you grow in your recovery and transformation, you'll find others.

In my early recovery, there were no L.I.F.E. Recovery Groups or faith based addiction recovery groups to attend where I lived. I was advised to go to any kind of 12-step group. So, I chose AA. I started going to a relatively large group and tried to "pass." I'm not an alcoholic so I would just say that I was an "addict." No one seemed to mind at first. Then one of the men asked me, "Mark, just what kind of addict are you?" So, I told my story. It turned out that he struggled with the same kind of addictive behaviors. Over the next weeks we told our stories to a variety of the men who came to AA. Before we knew it, there were

20 men coming to a group meeting, that we started, that more specifically met our need. My belief is that the Holy Spirit will direct your story telling. God will always bring people to you, and you will feel that tug at your heart, that they need to hear your story. Trust your feelings and be of good courage.

Now, I don't mean you should rush out and tell your story to everyone. (That's not practicing healthy boundaries.) You may have that temptation, because part of you just wants to tell the whole world and get the truth out there. You might think spilling all would be a great catharsis a cleansing of your soul. But you need to be careful so that you don't share indiscriminately with those who might not be safe, or that you may harm by your story. Do you tell your story so that you feel better, or so that it may help another? When in doubt, always check out your desire to share your story with your group or your accountability network. Get their feedback about the appropriateness of sharing with a specific person. On the other hand, your group might also be able to encourage you when you need support.

Journaling Exercise: Sharing Your Story

List the names of four people who might need to hear your story:

1. _____

2. _____

3. _____

4. _____

Keep track in your journal of those times when you do share about your journey. In your journal record your feelings about what it was like to offer your "experience, strength, and hope." Describe the other person's reaction.

PRINCIPLE ONE
Assignment Three - Identifying our Roots and Desire

We admit that we have absolutely no control of our lives.
The sin of our addiction has become unmanageable.

Confronting Reality: I'm Shackled in My Own Prison

Congratulations! Despite long years of deceit, lies, denial, minimization, fears, shame, and manipulation, you have picked up this L.I.F.E. Recovery Guide or have come to a L.I.F.E. Recovery Group meeting. You have wanted to, thinking that perhaps you should, pondering if it was the right thing to do. You have resisted, found excuses, wondered who would find out, and worried about the consequences of getting honest. You've thought that no one would really understand. You've either believed that you have done the worst things possible – things no one else has ever done; or you've thought your stuff is not so bad - that you really don't need to come to a meeting and admit to others that you need help. Hear these words:

Welcome.
You're in the right place.
We're glad you're here.

That phrase, "the sin of my addiction," may stir some discomfort, if not down-right fear, for some. Addictive behavior is harmful to our physical body, mind, and spirit. During the time of "active addiction," we are living in rebellion to the will and plan of God, our Creator. In the Bible these acts of rebellion are called 'sin' and are revealed in our attitudes and behaviors that are against what God desires for us and from us. He created us to be His image incarnate, but rebellion entered into the Garden of Eden when our ancestors, Adam and Eve, disobeyed God by eating from the forbidden tree. Recognize that this act would not have taken place without there first being the attitude of rebellion against God and the decision made for the self to be in control; "to have it my way."

There are stories in the Bible called "parables:" earthly stories with a "moral" and a spiritual meaning. Imagine what it was like for the Prodigal Son. He was much like us in that he wanted to be in control of his own life. So he asked for, and received, his inheritance to underwrite his move to the city to start life on his own. Off he goes to the big city and engages in (what the Bible calls) "riotous living." He lived it up until the great economic depression (the Bible calls it a famine) came along, and the next thing he knew he had used up his resources. And there was no one to help him. (Isn't that just like "friends;" while you have plenty they are with you, but where are they when you are in need?) So he took a job (as we call it) 'slopping the hogs.' (Ironic isn't it; he's not "living high off the hog" now, is he?) This was an insult to a Jewish boy. He did not even have sustenance as good as the hogs. He decided that since the servants of his father were living better than he, he would go home and hire on as a servant to his father. He has suffered abandonment, rejection, humiliation, failure, depression, and who knows what else, and now he will add embarrassment as he goes crawling home to his father begging for a job.

Does any of this look like or sound like your experience? It is at this point that many turn to addictions, suicide, or insanity to cope with the pain of their predicament. What choices have you made? Some turn to partying, but the parties lead to other behaviors that lead to further problems. Sooner or later, the party is over, then what? The Prodigal Son just wanted to be home. He didn't think he deserved to return to his earlier status as a son because his sins were so great. He hoped merely to be (like) one of his father's hired servants. Maybe you're like that; you're just glad to be alive and able to get to a meeting. You'd like to simply be quiet and belong.

The Prodigal Son's father, however, rushed out to meet him (and don't miss this fine point: The Bible says that while he {the son} was yet *a long way off* {get those words} his father saw him {the father was looking and longing for his 'lost son'} and was filled with compassion. The father *ran* in view of the village, and threw his arms around his neck and kissed him to accept him fully and prepared a great feast. That is our picture of God's response to us. He is expectantly watching for your return.

There is great rejoicing when we come to or come back to our Heavenly Father. We in L.I.F.E. Recovery want to be imitators of God, "just like little children." It may feel like you're a little boy, or girl, who has just come on the bus or into the lunchroom or onto the playground, and you may be expecting to be rejected or at least ignored. Instead, someone rushes over to greet you! All of us have been where you've been. We understand your pain and your fears. We're glad you've come. God prepares hospitality like a feast. We can't prepare a literal great feast, but we can go to coffee later.

Many of our stories are very much like that of the Prodigal Son, and yet each will be very different in detail according to the experiences of our life's journey. Our results will depend on our choice to either face or hide from our past, present, and *expected* future consequences of our dependencies. For some, the pain of our past is more than we are equipped to manage successfully, so we hide from the pain of life we experience in the present. Trauma is a term we apply to painful experiences that overwhelm our physical, mental/emotional, and spiritual resources. *Acute* trauma is brief, less than four weeks, and we are able to regain our physical, mental/emotional, and spiritual 'footing' and return to a healthy life-style within a brief period of time. When the traumatic event, or events, persists beyond four weeks, we begin our search for relief from sources outside of ourselves, resorting to illicit drugs, alcohol, gambling, relationships, sex, work, or some other activity in which we can "lose ourselves" and "avoid the pain of living."

Eventually we find ourselves trapped in routine behaviors that are no longer working for us. It is for such a person that L.I.F.E. Recovery was given its vision and mission; to develop resources that help you find peace, and assist you with regaining "your footing" so as to return "home" to healthy living; physically, mentally and emotionally, and, most of all, spiritually (*"What does it profit a man if he gains the whole world, but loses his own soul?"* Matthew 16:26).

In a book entitled, *Ghosts from the Nursery*, the authors present extensive insight into the effects of early trauma experiences (physical, emotional, environmental) upon early development (the first 33 months – gestation to age 2) that have lifelong consequences, and to which we react (note that word as compared to "respond") without conscious awareness. Another purpose for the first assignment exercise is to *begin* processing the awareness of our root issues, family systems or family of origin work, to answer the question, "Why do I do the things I do?"

This impact on our present behaviors makes it necessary to take a deep look at your history and answer the question, "How did I get here?" If you were taking a long road trip and found yourself "lost," wouldn't it be prudent to first identify where you are and where you want to go, as well as how you got lost so you could plan an effective and efficient correction to your travel plans? We need to apply the same principle in planning our journey to healthier living.

We have to come to terms with the pain in our lives. We admit the pain to ourselves first, then admit our pain to God and then admit our pain to others. Sharing your pain with others is possibly the most difficult of all, but it is in safe relationships where we begin to heal and learn to speak the truth that our lives have become unmanageable.

Your first assignment is simply to get honest with yourself. We know that the greatest enemy of our being open and honest is silence; you have been deceived to think that silence has been your friend in the sense that your silence has enabled you to continue in your addiction to the behavioral choices that you have continually made to ease the pain of life. We also know how carefully you've guarded the secrets of your dependencies, habits, or behaviors. It's hard to imagine letting your secrets out. These were your comfort, safety, retreat and reward. There are thoughts in your mind telling you, "No! You can't talk about that. Someone will go running and screaming out of the room!" Or "You did what?" and turn away from you. We encourage you to confront those demons: those voices that have kept you shackled in your pain for too long.

We know your fears of shame and rejection because we are on a similar journey of learning to live in freedom every day. We want you to tell us how bad your pain and acting out got and what it was like to feel powerless over your life. Chances are that others in your group have done some of the same things, had some of the same feelings. There is nothing, certainly no behavior or habit, that separates you from the love of God. (See Romans 8:35) No matter what you've thought or what you've done, it's time to come home to the heavenly Father who loves you and is longing for your freedom; He is waiting for you. (John 8:36: *"If the Son makes you free, you shall be free indeed."* Romans 8:2: *". . .the Spirit of life in Christ Jesus has made me free. . ."*)

The assignment that you are about to undertake will take great courage. It will seem to be a risk and a challenge. Don't turn back now. Keep putting one foot in front of the other and head for home. The freedom you will experience in being in real community is worth all it will take to get there. *("Being confident of this very thing, that He Who started a good work in you will carry it on to completion until the day of Christ Jesus."* Philippians 1:6) Trust in Him to rush out to meet you and guide you when the going gets tough. He will provide for you, strengthen you, and welcome you home! He will work through your L.I.F.E. Recovery Group when and if you let Him. You need the group, and the group needs you. It is in the safety of a L.I.F.E. Recovery Group that you can find your voice and learn to speak truth without fear. Welcome, you're home!

Assignment Three - Identifying our Roots and Desire

As you've worked through the Principles you should now have a pretty good grasp on how truly powerless you have been over your addiction. I hope you're making progress in accepting responsibility for your sinful behavior, seeking accountability, and connecting in genuine fellowship with others. It's time now for you to examine the core causes that have contributed to your addiction.

We suggest that you have a solid foundation of sobriety and support before you begin probing into the underlying issues. You may have already noticed in your work thus far that many feelings have come up for you that you've historically sought to medicate.

Stop for a moment. Stirring up painful feelings may seem like a problem to you. Perhaps you've been one of those Christians who have believed that once you start making the right decisions, like getting sober, everything will just automatically get better. You may have thought that you won't experience negative consequences; that your spouse and others would immediately start trusting you; that you wouldn't lose important relationships, your employment, your standing in the community, or face financial chaos. Most of all, you've thought that you would be "happy." You're disappointed and discouraged that you continue to feel tough emotions.

Welcome to reality! Your journey toward living in freedom every day is just that – a journey. The road won't always be clear or the way smooth. Making right choices won't exempt you from painful consequences or difficult emotions. In fact, this beginning period of recovery is probably one of the hardest you'll ever experience. For so long your emotions have been covered by your acting out, until you probably didn't feel anything at all most of the time. And guess what? When you do begin to feel, the first emotions are almost always the painful ones.

The period of time between the third and the ninth months of recovery is a really dangerous time for a variety of reasons. First, you might be experiencing the violation of expectations that I just described. And your reaction might be anger. Perhaps you're saying to yourself, "What's the use of being in a healing journey if this is all I get? I thought my life would be better by now." You could also be angry about all the restrictions in your life because of your recovery program. There seem to be so many things that have been taken away. You may hate being an "addict." You believe you're not normal, and you feel strange. You may be getting tired of all the hard work.

Relax. You are normal. Remember that even though you call yourself an addict now, that word doesn't define you. You are a precious child of God. You are fearfully and wonderfully made. Yes, you are a person who has suffered with addiction, but you are much more than that. Be gentle with yourself.

Journaling Exercise: Your Positive Qualities

> *In the first part of this assignment make a list of the positive qualities about yourself. If you can't think of any, ask some of your group members to help you.*

Now that you have reminded yourself of some of your positive attributes, you can move on. *(However, don't forget that you need to work your program just as hard now as you did in the first few weeks.)* It's time to go deeper into your thoughts and feelings. It's time to get to some of the root causes of your loneliness and anger.

WOUNDS FROM YOUR FAMILY

Please start by doing some reading in other places about family of origin issues. There are a wide variety of good options. Check out the resource section listed on the L.I.F.E Recovery's website at www.freedomeveryday.org. Also, Tim Clinton and Gary Sibcy have written a book, *Why You Love, Feel, and Act the Way You Do* that is an excellent, easy-read regarding family of origin issues and the traumatic results as well as how God is the healing resource to help families become all that He has designed for us. To go deeper in understanding how you came to have the difficulties that have caused struggles in your life, especially if you have struggled with anger and/or violence issues that you have sought to medicate, I recommend *Ghosts from the Nursery* by Robin Karr-Morse, Meredith S. Wiley, and T. Berry Brazelton, MD. This book presents insight to the environment and developmental hazards of early childhood and the negative effects.

I think it's important to remember the purpose for understanding the origin of the influences in our development. It's not to blame our parents or others for our problems. Blaming doesn't solve anything. Nor is the point to try to justify our behaviors. The point is to gain understanding, which we can use to help us change our behavior and further our healing.

I have come to some more complete understandings of how we should think about our family of origin. We used to make the distinction between coming from an unhealthy or dysfunctional family and a healthy or functional family. That put many of us in a rather difficult position. Many of us had a hard time with this. We thought that we came from a rather nice family. We may have been rather protective of them and really not wanted to get into all these memories of problems. This is a rather natural resistance. We have been taught as Christians to love and honor our families. We do in fact love them and probably need them.

I've decided that our thinking in these matters gets too black and white. Do we really need our families to be either "good" or "bad?" I believe that all families are families that do many good and loving things, and that all families make mistakes. I know that I've made many mistakes as a father. Does that make me a dysfunctional dad? I hope that it makes me a father who loves his kids and tries his best. I believe that is true of those parents in life who make horrendous mistakes. Some of them are acting out of their own woundedness, immature and selfish even to the point of really terrible things happening but as you will see as we outline the healing journey, we shouldn't get stuck in trying to decide how good or bad they are. That is ultimately up to God to decide.

In my experience, I have found that some of us have felt what I call "family of origin shame." This can take two different paths. One of them is to think that we come from the worst possible family. Our story is really bad, our parents really terrible, and wounds really damaging. We might even be tempted to think that it is no wonder we committed so many sins — our history is just a nightmare. We can also get competitive in thinking that our story is the "worst." The other path is to feel shame because we really can't think of that many bad things that our family did. Now we're in trouble. How could we have committed terrible sins, when there doesn't seem to be any root cause? Those of you who feel this way start worrying that the problem is really you and that thought is really shameful. We might even start thinking about "inventing" some stories about our family so that we can "fit in."

Even the therapeutic community is concerned about this last possibility. There is a debate that goes on about something called "False Memory Syndrome." The belief by some is that therapists can help a person create memories that didn't really happen. For example, if a therapist has ever said to you, "80% of all sex addicts are sexual abuse survivors, you must be one too," you might need to be careful.

Over the years I have found that the best approach is always the way of prayer. As you begin this assignment, take a moment every time you work on it and ask God to help you remember the events of the past that you need healing from. Tell God that you are willing to heal them and that you are not just looking for excuses. Tell God that you have a lot of pain, loneliness, and anger and you are wondering where it comes from and then ask Him to show you. Always be in counseling or in groups that remind you to engage in this kind of prayer. Therapists, pastors and groups only guide and encourage you in this prayerful journey; *they are not to suggest* to you what really happened.

As you work through this material about your family, let me summarize some of the issues that you should be aware of:

- The **rules** that existed in your family. Think of examples of how your family taught you to express your feelings, to talk, and to accept responsibility. Or did your family blame, minimize, or deny responsibility, or *not* talk, *not* feel?
- The **roles** that were played out in your family. Examples include the heroine or saint, the little princess, the scapegoat, the mascot, the doer, the martyr, and the peacekeeper.
- What boundaries did, or did not, your family observe? Were they healthy **boundaries**? Did you feel safe? Did you feel loved, protected, nurtured, and affirmed?
- What **addictions,** if any, were present in your family? Some of these might have been substances and others might have been behaviors or processes. If there was an addict, who were the enablers?
- Was there any emotional, physical, sexual, or spiritual **abuse**?

- Are there any **abandonment** experiences that you remember? Do you feel that your needs were met? Were you affirmed, heard, protected, touched, and desired? Understand that it's often hard to identify ways we can be abandoned in a family (even if both parents are present in the home); how do you know you missed something that you never had?

Journaling Exercises: Your Family

- *What were the main <u>rules</u> that existed in your family.*

- *What were the primary <u>roles</u> you played in your family? What roles did others play?*

- *Consider the <u>boundaries</u> in your family. Were they too loose? Too rigid? Or a combination of both?*

- *What <u>addictions</u> were present in your family, identity of the addict(s).*

- *What forms of <u>abuse</u> did you experience? Who were the perpetrator(s)?*

- *In what ways were you <u>abandoned</u>? When did you feel lonely, frightened, left out, different, or weird? Can you describe times of feeling that no one cared or wanted you?*

NOTE: Remember, you may need more information about family dynamics in order to understand them fully and to complete this journaling exercise. Refer to "Why You Love, Feel, and Act the Way You Do", or a similar source for a thorough explanation.

Connecting with the Comforter

I know I'm asking you to do some very painful work. You may resist delving into these feelings. You may even be feeling anxious or unsafe. I encourage you to pause for a few moments and conduct an imagery exercise at this point. It's important to only undertake this work with the comfort and presence of your heavenly Father.

Create, if you can, an image in your mind. Refer to the Bible story recorded in Matthew 19:13-15 about the little children Jesus welcomed after the disciples had tried to keep them away. - Imagine that you are one of those children. You really want to sit on Jesus' lap, but there is something that keeps you from doing so. Perhaps you're afraid you'll bother him, or worse, that you'll be ridiculed or rejected. You can't imagine that Jesus really wants to spend time with you.

Then, in your mind, let your eyes meet those of Jesus, and hear His words of invitation, *"Come to me."* The Lord reaches out His hand and beckons you closer. When you climb up on His lap, imagine that He comforts you and He tells you how much He loves you.

Then Jesus gently asks, *"What are you feeling, my child? What is it like to be you?"* Remember, you aren't an adult in this image, but a child. Be honest with Jesus. Tell Him about your experiences growing up in your family. Share your hurts and fears. He can hear you and understand. He already knows what it was like for you. He wants you to say it.

Journaling Exercise: Conversation with Jesus

> *Describe in your journal what this conversation with Jesus was like. Write the things you told Him. Take as long as you need and simply allow the feelings to surface. When you're through, consider making a special effort to talk with someone from your L.I.F.E. Recovery Group about this exercise.*

Trauma Reactions

The principle of why we do this hard work is simple. The after effects of trauma don't go away by themselves. Painful memories have a way of surfacing and creating feelings. Have you ever had someone, like your spouse, say, "You're overreacting!" or "Why did something so trivial create such a large reaction?" When the intensity of our response doesn't match the precipitating event, it's a clear sign we've been triggered by the pain of the past. Sometimes, these reactions to the past come in forms other than overreaction. You may think that someone is angry with you, and they say they're not. In that case, you're probably reacting to earlier times when a key person was angry in a similar situation. Or do you find yourself suddenly getting sad at some song, movie, TV show, or event, when no one else around seems to be having that reaction? Likewise, do you ever find yourself getting angry at something, and it just doesn't make sense?

These are examples of "flashbacks" to times when older feelings are affecting your current reaction. In essence, we are re-experiencing the event as if it was happening, or about to happen, in the present moment. There is a distinct difference between "remembering" an event and "re-experiencing" the event. "Re-experiencing" includes re-living the event with its emotional content, while "remembering" is recalling an event, including the emotional content, without re-living the emotional content of the event. I can, still today, very vividly recall the abuse of my childhood without provoking the emotions of fear that I experienced at the time.

A "trigger" is the term for any stimulus that brings up older feelings.

One person has related the experience of being at the funeral of a woman who was the mother of a best friend. "When they closed the casket I felt intense feelings of sadness and started to cry. Now, I hardly knew the deceased woman. What it reminded me of is the death of my own mother. She died four years ago." His sadness was for his own mother. Over the years there are many things he noticed that trigger him into sadness or anger about his mother. For example:

- When one of her favorite hymns is played
- When he saw a woman who acts or looks like her
- Crossword puzzles (one of her favorite things to do)
- The month of February (the month in which she died) and anything about the month like the events of the month, the temperature outside, snow, etc.
- His wife saying no to sex
- Anything any woman says that suggests rejection to him

This is a partial list but it does give you examples of how broad and how trivial these triggers can be. Do you get the idea? If he is in a conversation with his wife, for example, and his old feelings are "triggered" they can affect his current reaction to his wife even though these feelings were really about his mother.

Here's an important principal:

Because your woundedness creates the pain that drives your addiction, you need to heal your oldest feelings first. Later feelings will follow, and your healing journey will be more successful. Again, we remind you of the importance of being in counseling to resolve the deep emotions that are the result of your traumatic experiences.

Your current issues may be the latest evolution or manifestation of wounds that you have experienced since childhood. We have a way of repeating old issues, hoping for healing, and we're frustrated when they never seem to go away. It's crucial that you get beneath the obvious problem to the deeper issues, which probably date back to childhood. The deeper you go into your core wounding the more you are able to find healing.

Eight Specific Trauma Reactions

We all have a variety of ways that we cope with our wounds from the past. Some of us avoid our feelings at all costs. Or we may use addictive activity to medicate those feelings. In his book *The Betrayal Bond*, Patrick Carnes talks about eight possible reactions to our wounds. You may want to read Carnes' book to get a more detailed description of these reactions. In addition to your individual reading, it might be good for your L.I.F.E. Recovery Group to spend some time discussing these reactions.

For now, let me list them briefly.

1. **Blocking.** This refers to any behavior or substance that you use to avoid your feelings. Consider how this might be manifested in your life. You've already thought about alcohol or drugs (legal prescriptions illegally used or illegal drugs), and other behaviors, (such as gambling, sex, etc.) Don't forget those socially acceptable substances like caffeine and nicotine, or food. Make sure you also include what would be considered

"positive" behaviors (like work). Sleeping a lot is another example you may not have considered. The effect of blocking is that you're "numbing" yourself. I often refer to this as "going to the land of numb."

2. **Splitting**. The clinical community refers to this reaction as "dissociating." When you split, you "leave," mentally checking out. You may be lost in thoughts, daydreaming, or even having fantasies. Rape victims are frequently known to leave their bodies and emotionally go to someplace far away. It's like that for some trauma survivors: their minds go far away.

3. **Abstinence**. This reaction means that you avoid any stimulus that reminds you of the trauma. Some sexual trauma survivors, for example, avoid sex altogether. This pattern is called "sexual anorexia," which is about avoidance. Abstinence can be very specific, such as avoiding certain sexual behaviors. For some, this pattern is a form of self-deprivation: a means of avoiding success, or eating, or spending. Spending, for example, reminds them of not having money and thus activates their fear of poverty.

4. **Reactions**. This one is a broad category that refers to any way your mind or your body tells you that you're afraid. You may have dreams that wake you up in the middle of the night. You might experience "flashbacks" or sudden memories that suddenly leap into your mind. Your body may develop aches and pains that don't seem related to any medical condition. Stomachaches, backaches, and headaches are examples. Some chronic pain conditions, like fibromyalgia, could also point to a chronic fear of harm. Any stress-related symptoms could fit into this category.

5. **Repetition**. This reaction means that a person seeks to repeat experiences of trauma for two main possible reasons. First, he might hope for a different outcome. Why do some people seem to keep going back to damaging relationships or situations? It's because of their hope that this time the situation will be resolved or the relationship will work. The language of AA refers to this pattern as the definition of insanity, when we keep doing the same thing and hoping for a different result. Second, a person might repeat a traumatic situation. Some sexual trauma survivors, for example, rather than avoid sex, engage in promiscuous sex, this time trying to be the one who is in the power position, rather than the one who's being harmed. There is the mistaken notion that by being in control, the pain of earlier memories will be diminished. This form of trauma repetition is sometimes referred to as the "victim to victimizer" cycle and is often behind offending behaviors.

6. **Bonds**. This pattern describes finding others who will help you play out old situations. When this person "bonds," he gets into relationships with people who remind him in some way of the person(s) who created the original harm. Examine your relationships and ask if you aren't seeking to replay old patterns with this person for either of the reasons described in the paragraph above about trauma repetition. In the cartoon strip "Peanuts," for example, why does Charlie Brown keep going back to a spiteful Lucy, who always pulls the football away?

7. **Pleasure**. This trauma reaction is one of the most painful patterns, possibly literally. People who have this pattern find pleasure in pain. Those who get involved with sado-masochistic behavior, for example, find sexual high from painful situations. Others engage in other high risk behaviors that inflict pain. It could be that they are recreating situations from their past - ones in which they found the only touch or attention they ever received involved pain. It could also mean that the excitement and adrenalin, or the fear and danger involved get neurochemically programmed in their brain. This person becomes addicted to the rush of his own neurochemistry in painful or threatening situations.

8. **Shame**. Old wounds create the core belief that "I am a defective and, therefore, worthless person." People who experience trauma shame don't know how to be happy or content. They find a sense of identity from feeling shameful. They can often play the victim or martyr role.

Don't be frightened by these trauma reactions. With the help of your L.I.F.E. Recovery Group and possibly a therapist, you can gain important insights from identifying which reactions apply to you. Understanding them can help you create new behaviors and boundaries that will break these patterns. You don't have to remain shackled to the traumas of the past! You can experience the abundant L.I.F.E. that Jesus offers.

Journaling Exercise: Your Trauma Reactions

> *Note in your journal which trauma reactions apply to you. Describe specifically how you experience them.*

This next exercise may cause significant fear due to the fact that objectively considering your own fantasies may trigger loss of self-control and ultimately relapse into unwanted addictive behaviors. **Therefore it is important that you complete this section in piecemeal fashion, with the support of a trusted friend or advisor in order to reduce the potential for relapse.**

First, a principle:

Fantasy, or preoccupied thoughts, are an attempt to resolve traumatic pain.

Our fantasies are an attempt to create an ideal world or scenario in which all of our wounds are healed. Think about it, fantasies are the way in which we 'correct' pain from our past. It's pain about who we really are. Fantasies may correct our sense of who we are. In our fantasies we are powerful, successful, and lovable; or so we believe. In our fantasies we get touched, praised, nurtured, and affirmed. We are immensely desirable.

Take athletic fantasies for example. Don't many of us have those? In them we find athletic greatness. We are stars, and receive adulation. I have many basketball fantasies in which I correct all the mistakes, the losses, the failures of the past. What about fantasies about physical appearance? Perhaps we fantasize about people turning their heads and noticing us.

What about money fantasies? In mine, I have all the money I need for anything, so I pursue gambling, or, specifically, playing the lottery, or other schemes of chance. I might win the lottery and have houses, cars, boats, and planes. People love me and want to be with me because I am so rich. Now turn to sexual fantasies. What are you correcting? It may simply be that you aren't getting enough sex, at least in your own mind. You need to be desired and affirmed. You need to be touched. You need to feel like you are admired and valued. Everybody wants you and would just die to be with you and would do anything for you.
It may be more complicated than that. Before we go any further, do this exercise. Be careful. I am going to ask you to describe your most common fantasy. Try not to get into it too far. Be an observer of it, not a participant in it. Answer the following four questions about what seems to be the fantasy that you are the most likely to play out in your mind. It may be the most recent. It may be the one that you have played out a thousand or more times over the course of your life. It may have variations. The people may have changed. Distill out the **theme**. Don't be graphic. Your fantasy themes, like the examples above, might involve many scenarios: work, physical appearance, drugs (illicit or prescription), alcohol, anger, money, sex, romance… you get the idea. Yes, I did insert anger; 1) to see if you would notice it, and 2) to identify an emotion that we use just as we would use other forms of addiction acting out – to "numb" our pain by manipulating situations that are disturbing to us or are out of our control.

In your fantasy, or when you daydream that *"it'll be better when…"*

1. What is the nature of the activity? Be specific about it, but not detailed. As mentioned before, include fantasies about your performance in sports, gaming, business, relationships, does it involve your appearance, money, fame, or success. Be fearless as you describe this. Please note, your fantasy description is to be general but not graphic.

2. How will you feel when you get the substance, the lottery ticket, the piece of cake, the gambling game, on the internet, cosmetic enhancement, new clothing or possession, or whatever activity that distracts you from the present uncomfortable, if not unbearable situation? Describe the emotion that you will feel, is it contentment, relief, relaxation, calmness, peace?

3. Where will you obtain your "fix?" Do you have it handy; a ready resource? How will you get your need met?

4. Where does the use or consumption take place? What is the setting, the mood, and the atmosphere? Do you have a favorite place; favorite people with whom you will share your experience?

Most of you will discover that perhaps only one of these four categories stands out to you. You may not care who shows up as long as a certain activity takes place. What *is important* to you can be *really* important.

Be courageous. Be honest. Secrets hinder intimacy. Remember, your secrets concerning your addiction have kept you in bondage. There is no sin that can separate you from the love of God. Now, once you have the description of your most common fantasy, the main question is what does it mean to you?

- *Ask yourself, what does it suggest to you about your needs? Remember the principle that this fantasy could be your attempt to heal wounds.*

We should not forget that there may be other reasons why you have this fantasy. It could be based on actual life experiences that were really exciting to you. It could be the result of the adrenalin that you have created in thinking it up. My guess is that even if these things are true, the fantasy speaks to the deepest longings of your heart for love and nurture, for relief from the stresses in your living situations. "I want to feel - better, - more relaxed, - more in control, - more connected with others."

Why are your fantasies important? If it is true that this fantasy is an attempt to heal a part of your soul, when you seek to shut this fantasy off, it will quiet the voice of your soul. You must give voice to the deepest longing of your soul. If you don't, it will find other ways to talk to you. It craves to be heard, perhaps just as you did when you were a child. If you can hear that voice, and find healthy ways to heal the wounds, your fantasies will go away. You won't need them.

Talk with your group about what are better answers to your need for affirmation, praise, touch, nurture, safety, and to belong.

First, as Christians, we know that the main answer to resolving the wounding of our value is in a relationship with God through his Son Jesus Christ. Secondly, we maintain that truth in fellowship with other Christians. In your relationship with God you must come to understand that He loves you *just as you are*. There is no sin that stops Him from loving you. In your relationship with others, you must find safety, affirmation, healthy relational interaction, and a true sense of belonging.

Ask God to teach you what your fantasy means and how you can find more ultimate fulfillment in a deepening relationship with Him. Journal about this and discuss it with your group and/or your therapist.

PRINCIPLE TWO
Assignment Three – Placing Hope in God

*We believe in God, accept the grace offered through
His Son, Jesus Christ, and surrender our lives and
our wills to Him on a daily basis.*

Finding the Solution: I Have Only One Option

In the book of John, chapter 5, there is a memorable and dramatic story of one of Jesus' healing miracles. As the account records, outside of Jerusalem is a pool called Bethesda, which was known as a place of healing. Occasionally an angel would come down and stir the water, and whoever got into the pool first was healed. One paralyzed man had been lying there for 38 years.

When Jesus came on the scene and saw this paralyzed, despairing man, the Great Physician asked an unusual question. Now think for a moment. If you were the one who encountered this paralyzed man, what would you say? Perhaps you would say something like, "That must be tough," or "How can I help you get into the pool?" You might be wondering about this man's condition.

Instead of one of those expected responses, Jesus asks a different question: *"Do you want to get well?"* To us, that sounds rather stupid. Why wouldn't a man who has been lying by a healing pool for 38 years want to get well?

But Jesus is the master psychologist. He knows what to ask to probe into the heart of our paralysis: **"Do you want to get well?"**

Assignment Three – Placing Hope in God

I invite you to do an imaginative exercise somewhat like you did when you considered your most frequent fantasy regarding the use of your acting out behaviors. This time, though, you'll be imagining a scene that springs from hope, instead of one that comes from the pain of the past. First, if your description or picture of God (Assignment Two of this Principle) is of an angry or distant Being, recreate (at least in your mind) an image that more accurately portrays God as a God of love, mercy, and grace.

Now I want you to see yourself interacting with that kind of God. This is the "Abba" God – the intimate "daddy" God (Mark 14:36; Romans 8:15; Galatians 4:6). This is the God who would have you ride on His shoulders, throw ball with you, listen to your stories, and comfort your fears. He is the perfect father. (A good description of this biblical view of God may be found in Sandra Wilson's *Into Abba's Arms* or in many of the writings by Max Lucado.)

Imagine the two of you talking and laughing together. Try to picture some specific activity or conversation. Observe all the details of the setting. Let this scene become real in your mind.

You can be confident that God is truly the loving, caring Abba Father you imagined. It's safe to depend on Him, because He is 100% trustworthy. To surrender to God is to place your life and will into the care of One who is eager to be in relationship with you. God loved you enough that He sent His only Son to die on the cross for your sins.

The connection you've sought through sinful addiction practices is really the longing for intimacy with God. Your passion is to be known and loved and cherished, despite your faults. Only God can fulfill that desire. Intimacy with Him can never be found through pursuit of the flesh.

An important part of your transformation process will be to experience the fathering of your Abba God. Only His love and the grace of Christ can sustain and heal you. All other substitutes are false. And the path to this intimacy with God begins with surrender.

Journaling Exercise: Placing Hope in God

1. *Write a description of the above encounter with God in your journal. Be specific; include as much detail as possible. What did you do? How did God respond? What did you say to each other? Share your image with someone from your L.I.F.E. Recovery Group.*
2. *Compose a statement of surrender to God. (The Third Step Prayer of AA is an example.) Remember, the wording and grammar isn't important. The intent of your heart is what matters. Offer the prayer at your next group meeting or share it with your pastor or accountability partner.*

Two passages of Scripture seem particularly appropriate to this Principle about putting our hope in God and surrendering totally our wills to Him:

"Come to Me, all you who labor and are heavy laden,
and I will give you rest.
Take My yoke upon you and learn from Me,
for I am gentle and lowly in heart,
and you will find rest for your souls.
For My yoke is easy and My burden is light."

- Matthew 11: 28-30

"If anyone desires to come after Me,
let him deny himself, and take up his cross, and follow Me.
For whoever desires to save his life will lose it,
and whoever loses his life for My sake will find it.
For what is a man profited if he gains the whole world, and loses his own soul?
Or what will a man give in exchange for his soul?"

- Matthew 16: 24-26

PRINCIPLE THREE
Assignment Three - Confessing Our Darkness

We make a list of our sins and weaknesses, and
confess those to a person of spiritual authority.

Telling the Truth: I Must Leave the Darkness

Your earlier work in Principle One called for you to admit to yourself and your L.I.F.E. Recovery Group the truth about your sin of addiction coming with choices and behaviors not in the will of God that medicate the emotional pain of your history. In Principle Two you affirmed that God is trustworthy and faithful to transform your life, if you surrender to Him. Principle Three confronts your sinful nature, and eventually prompts you to confess your sins to others.

Working on Principle Three will be painful, just as it was painful to complete the exercises of Principle One. This kind of pain, actually, can be very helpful in the journey of transformation. *Confession to another human being* as well as to God reminds us of how far we are from God. The sting in our heart teaches us to turn to Him. Experiencing consequences forces us to let go of control. A tender conscience motivates us to refrain from causing more harm. Don't be afraid of the pain of these assignments, but instead, walk through it to the place of living in freedom everyday.

Principle Three challenges you to understand your dark side – your sinful nature. We are all sinners and fall short of the glory of God, according to Paul. We are inheritors of original sin: *the sin of pride* which tempts us to take control, rather than to be submitted to God's guidance and provision. Your addicted self – your sinful self – has pridefully and, perhaps at the core, fearfully tried to hide the truth about your life. You've believed that you are bad and worthless and that others wouldn't love you if they really knew you, especially if they knew how and why you've medicated. You've feared that if people knew your secrets, they would hate you and leave you. These descriptions illustrate a principle known as "**intimacy disorder,**" which will be discussed more toward the end of this assignment.

Assignment Three - Confessing Our Darkness

This assignment is quite simple, but extremely vital to your spiritual recovery. In James 5:16, the brother of Jesus tells us that we should "confess our sins to one another…so that you may be healed." This assignment is your time to make a confession in a formal way. By "formal" I mean in a way that is spiritually significant to you.

Take note that this is Assignment Three of Principle Three. This L.I.F.E. Recovery Guide hasn't asked you to do confession sooner because you needed to take the time to carefully consider your life. The timing was also designed to keep you from rushing out and confessing to everyone who came along, which is a temptation for some. These people believe that if they confess and get it over with, everything will be right with their world. This kind of shallow confession can feel cathartic, and may be dangerous. It's not appropriate to confess to everyone.

Here are several questions to reflect on as you prepare for this assignment:

1. Have you done serious and prayerful work on the first two assignments of Principle Three?

2. Have you looked at all areas of your life, not just those directly related to the acting out behaviors surrounding your addiction(s)?

3. Have you considered your reason for confessing at this time? What do you hope to accomplish? To be instantly forgiven by everyone? To be done with this painful process forever?

I remember a famous evangelist years ago who publicly confessed his sins on his TV show. He cried and lamented, then he quoted a variety of scriptures about God's grace and how we all need to forgive each other. There was something about his presentation and attitude that didn't feel quite right. Not surprisingly, several months later he relapsed with the same behaviors.

For confession to be genuine, it must occur according to these important guidelines:

- Confession is done out of brokenness and humility, not arrogance. There can be no sense of pride associated with confession; brokenness and pride cannot co-exist.
- Don't confess to anyone whose forgiveness you might be trying to manipulate.
- How others respond to your confession is their responsibility; some will receive your confession with joy, though they may experience hurt and anger; others will receive your confession, but then turn you away; and still others will not receive your confession. Remember, confession is agreeing with the offended regarding the harm you have done to them.
- Don't confess if you expect that this is the one and only time. We are forgiven once and it is done; however, we may need to confess our weakness in the flesh many times in our journey.
- Don't confess if you're just trying to get it over with.

Don't confess if you're thinking that others will be mad at you if you don't. Remember, confession is a genuine act of repentance, not something you do because you got caught. Confessing with a motive other than to acknowledge wrong doing and the sorrow for having done so, is insincere and manipulative.

Pray and mull over these parameters for authentic confession. Then get some feedback from your L.I.F.E. Recovery Group about your motivation and readiness to take this step at this time.

We also need to consider one other aspect of confession: our confession to God. I'm aware of how perfunctory or ritualistic this aspect of confession may have become for many of us. Most often it involves nothing more than a brief and nonspecific admission of sins done collectively at a church services. We might read together something printed in the bulletin, or we might pray silently to God about our sins. Those acts aren't enough. Confession is a *sacred* act to be done with God. It is also something that should be done with a person of spiritual authority. Consider who represents spiritual authority for you. Part of your thinking should consider the role of authority in the Church. Do you believe that God calls some to be pastors and evangelists and that they've been given spiritual authority to represent God's grace? Today, who do you say is "my pastor"?

Be careful here and don't automatically assume that it's your current pastor. Maybe you don't have a current pastor because you don't have a regular church relationship. Maybe you have been hurt by your current pastor. To begin, start with the religious traditions of your youth. Even though you may have converted to a different church body, you might still have a place in your heart that recognizes the spiritual authority of your childhood. I've talked to many people, for example, who have converted from Roman Catholicism to a Protestant denomination. But they still remember the spiritual authority of a priest, and their heart still warms at the thought of hearing words of forgiveness from the mouth of a priest.

So maybe your person of spiritual authority is someone from the past. Other possible candidates would be the person who led you to the Lord, a person who discipled or mentored you, a previous pastor, or a respected Bible teacher or Sunday School teacher. It might even be a Christian counselor or possibly the facilitator of your L.I.F.E. Recovery Group.

Journaling Exercise: Your Spiritual Authority

Write the names of a handful of people who represent spiritual authority to you.

_____

_____

_____

Now, is it possible to schedule an appointment with someone from your list to go over all the work you've done in Principle Three? These meetings sometimes take hours because there's so much to say, so you need to be sure the person has enough time available to hear you out.

After you've scheduled this appointment, write down the time in your journal. Then report this meeting to your L.I.F.E. Recovery Group, and ask the members to hold you accountable for keeping it. If it's not possible to meet with the first person on your list, keep going until you find someone who is available. Pray that the Lord will lead you to the right person. It could be someone that you don't know yet. I'll be honest with you, the first time I confessed my whole story it was to a retired Roman Catholic priest who was the chaplain at the treatment center where I was a patient. I didn't know him from Adam, but he was a person of spiritual authority to me, so when he said, "God forgives you," I believed.

My prayer is that you'll have a powerful encounter with the marvelous grace of God during this time of confession. I hope you'll find a listener who will be the ears and voice that reminds you of God's love and forgiveness.

Follow-up Journaling

After you've had this time of confession, journal about what it was like. You might write just a few sentences or paragraphs, or it may be longer. But it should be a definite entry in your journal that records this spiritual milestone.

As a final exercise, at your next L.I.F.E. Recovery Group use some time during check-in to report on your experience of confession. You might also, at some point, agree to be the person who does the talk on Principle Three for the appropriate meeting. Sharing what AA calls your "experience, strength, and hope" about confession would be a wonderful experience for you and a blessing to your fellow group members.

PRINCIPLE FOUR
Assignment Three – Cultivating Our Character

We seek accountability and to build our character
as children of God.

Growing in Transformation: I Mature in Character

Principle Four is about accountability and about character. In the early days of learning about accountability you may have many mistaken notions of what it means. As addicts, most of us resist the idea of being accountable. We don't like being told what to do. We bristle at the thought of having to check in with someone. When an accountability partner gives or withholds his permission for us to do certain things, we protest that we're being treated like a child. We question why we should submit to another person or allow someone else to control us so tightly.

(Now, be honest: Isn't your reaction fairly similar to what I just described?)

This independent, rebellious and prideful mindset is what makes most addicts resistant to the idea of accountability. It also represents many of the misconceptions about what it means to be accountable to someone for your recovery. A necessary part of healthy relationships is accountability to speak the truth. Accountability builds trust; trust builds healthy intimacy, that is, knowing one another. When the Bible speaks of "knowing," it is speaking of "experiencing" intimacy in the relationship. That word "intimacy," by the way, has nothing to do with 's-e-x' though sex may be involved. No, the intimacy of which I speak is openness, vulnerability. The word defines itself when it is broken down by syllables:

> IN – TI – MA – CY.
> IN – TO – ME – SEE (say that real fast – intomesee)

In Genesis 2:2 we read, *"And they were both naked* ('nakedness' may refer to 'nudity,' but also means 'fully exposed'), *the man and his wife, and were not ashamed."* There was no sin at this moment in time; all was pure and undefiled; there was no shame (dismay, disillusionment or disappointment that things did not turn out as expected) until sin entered. After sin, there was shame and they tried to hide. Our attempts to cover shame are also insufficient, just like Adam and Eve who tried to *"hide themselves from the presence of the Lord God."* God then questions us too, asking *"Where are you?"* Not because God doesn't know where we are, but rather that *we* need to acknowledge the facts of *where we are,* hence our confession and accountability to God and to one another. Being honest with our confession/accountability with God and others is vital for *our* health and the health of our relationships. Accountability is our protection against sin, our addiction behaviors.

Assignment Three – Cultivating Our Character

Principle Four is about growing in transformation and maturing in character. This assignment focuses on how we *cultivate* our character. In Galatians 5:19-21 we find a definitive description of the immature character, from which we now want to turn. Fortunately, we also have a detailed description of the mature character, referred to as the fruit of the Spirit that Paul describes in Galatians 5:22-26, that we are to pursue. Modeling ourselves after these qualities will be a lifetime journey. However, as you continue your journey of healing surrendered to the Holy Spirit you'll develop more and more of these character qualities.

One of the keys to the other qualities of character is the ability to be empathetic. **Empathy** is that ability to put yourself in the place of someone else, and to seek to understand what he or she is going through; to feel with them the pain they are, or have, experienced. Do you begin to see that your addiction has given you an opportunity to be more empathetic? You're beginning to understand your wounds, your pain, your loneliness, your anger, and your fear. This understanding will help you better understand those feelings in others. You'll be able to listen to their stories and understand their pain. You'll be more patient, kind, good, gentle, and peaceful. This change in character comes from your own humility.

This assignment is one piece in your ongoing journey to develop empathy. *Selfishness, of course, is the enemy of empathy.* Characteristically, most persons who are afflicted with addictive behaviors are very self-centered, otherwise described as *selfish.* Since most of us are turned off by the selfishness of others, why are we so often selfish? One formula I believe to be true is:

Selfishness is equal to unhealed wounds.

Selfish people are those who feel that their needs haven't been met. Selfish people are also those who think only *they* can meet their own needs. This belief is an aspect of the original sin, "I control my life; I don't trust God to do it." As you continue your work in recovery, you'll discover more and more that only God can sufficiently meet your needs. You'll also find, as some of your desires are being met through safe, intimate relationships with others, that you should become less selfish as you learn that there are healthy ways to have your needs met.

Empathy for Others

Empathy begins when you discover that others are wounded as you are. One of the great tasks of recovery is to understand that you're not alone in your wounds. As you listen to others in your L.I.F.E. Recovery Group, the universality of pain should become clear. As a way of aiding that process, Assignment Three asks you to do some rather strange things.

Journaling Exercise: Cultivating Empathy

1. *First, interview one of your accountability partners about the wounds they have experienced. Make a list of these wounds in your journal. (Obviously, ask their permission first. It's probably best to not identify this person by name.)*

2. *Now, pick a member of your family. It may be your spouse, a sibling, parent, or anyone else you feel safe with. (This person should have done some reflecting about his or her own life journey. Don't seek to educate this person or convince him of any wounds they haven't accepted or understood.) Interview this person about the wounds they've discovered about themselves, and write in your journal about what you learned in this interview.*

3. *Now, select a person that you may have hurt by your addictive behavior (perhaps by abandonment, involvement with the criminal justice system, loss of income to support family needs, etc.). Interview this person about the wounds they've experienced as the result of your behavior, and write in your journal about what you learned in this interview.*

4. *Follow this format with interviews of other significant individuals that have been hurt or disappointed by your addictive behaviors (such as missed work, missed family engagements [like missing your son's ball game, or daughter's piano recital], etc.).*

Let's continue with a rather dangerous assignment by imagining your last episode of acting out (your use of any substance or behavior to medicate, escape or serve as your "stress reliever") followed by promises to quit.

One of the basic truths about 'acting out' is that you use substances or behaviors to obtain what you need to bring relief to your emotional pain in an emotional crisis.

Journaling Exercise: Practicing Empathy

In your journal, write a few paragraphs that relate the impact that your addiction has had on others. What do you think it was like for these individuals? What pain or life challenges have they endured?

Affirming Others

Now, let's work on cultivating character in another direction. How are you at being affirming and encouraging to others? Many of us, since we were deprived of those positive strokes ourselves, have a hard time being affirming with others, particularly those whom we really love.

You might have to diligently practice this one. Make a conscious effort to be affirming and encouraging to others in your L.I.F.E. Recovery Group. When you give feedback to someone who has shared, start with an affirmation. Be encouraging before, during, and after meetings.

Now, consider those around you whom you love. Who do you suspect is really starved for affirmation and encouragement? Maybe it's your spouse. Remember that they might not be acting like they need encouragement because they're so angry or withdrawn. If you have children, they also need affirmation.

Journaling Exercise: Affirmation

Make a commitment to affirm someone close to you every day. Note in your journal what you did and how the person reacted.

Reflect on those who have affirmed and encouraged you in your life. It may not have been the person, or persons, you hoped it would be, like your mom or dad. It may have been a favorite teacher, coach, or other person who had a positive impact in your life. Do you remember how kind and generous and patient and loving that person was to you? Wouldn't you like to offer those gifts to someone else?

I've seen some miraculous changes in other people when I've simply taken the time to affirm them. Imagine the smile on someone's face who might delight in your encouraging words.

You'll find that if you carry out these assignments, your character will improve. You'll become more patient, kind, gentle, and self-controlled. Why is this? It is, of course, your ability to be empathetic. Do you see how important it is to cultivate your character in this area?

NOTE: If you find you have a hard time affirming others, go back to the anger section, and continue to work on your core woundedness. Remember that there is no shame in talking to a pastor, counselor, or trusted friend.

Journaling Exercise: From Scripture

Finally, remember again that character formation is a lifetime journey. Affirm yourself for finally thinking about these things, and taking them seriously.

Study two separate, but related, scriptures, and consider the words of Christ:
Luke 6: 27-49
Matthew 7: 1-12
Write in your journal your thoughts about these two teachings.

PRINCIPLE FIVE
Assignment Three - Living Amends

We explore the damage we have done, accept responsibility, and make amends for our wrongs.

Demonstrating Real Change: I Accept Responsibility

Principle Five marks a turning point in your journey of transformation. Here's a review of your work to this point as guided by the first four Principles. In Principle One you have come to admit to the unmanageability of your life because of the sin of your acting out behaviors that have demonstrated your inability or unwillingness to trust God with your problems, and your inability to solve problems on your own using methods that have actually multiplied the problems. In Principle Two you chose to surrender your addiction totally to Christ, and to seek God's will for your life on a daily basis. Through your work in Principle Three you have inventoried your history with complete honesty, and through specific confession to God, to self, and to another person, you have revealed the truths you have discovered. In Principle Four, you have sought an accountability partner, as part of the accountability team, to address your flaws and inadequacies of character by entering into relationships of accountability as a matter of support and to maintain honesty with yourself.

These flaws and inadequacies stem from earlier woundedness and while learning to communicate these realities requires an expression of feelings and processing pain, these skills then develop into healthy interaction necessary for intimate relationships. These first four Principles are vitally foundational for genuine, lasting change. You have examined the depth of your sinful nature and your need for God, and you have taken the huge steps of telling the truth and asking for help.

Your journey thus far, though, has been largely self-focused. These examinations, confessions, and submission to accountability have required, and will continue to require, great introspection; you're looking inward and exploring your life, behavior, mind, and heart.

Principle Five expands your investigation. It will challenge you to look outside of yourself, and consider the ways your sin, your addictive acting out behaviors, has impacted others. You will continue to admit that you're not isolated in your sin, can*not* be isolated in your sin, and that it has repercussions for others. The effects of your addictive behaviors are like a pebble tossed into a pool of water: there are rings of ripples in the water that are ever multiplying, ever expanding; so with the expanding 'circles of influence' of our addictive acting out behaviors. The people known to you in your life, and people **not** known to you, are affected by your addictive acting out. Your actions have caused pain for many, probably more than you'd like to think. Your behavior and character flaws have harmed others in a variety of ways you have not considered. The process of Principle Five begins with a thorough assessment of the damage caused by your sin, its consequences, character flaws resulting from your woundedness, and the cause of your sinful behavior. Like Nehemiah, you will venture outside yourself to survey the damage that exists in your environment; you

will observe the fallout of your life; you will catalog the pain you've caused for others; and you will look unflinchingly at the harm you've brought about.

As in Principle One Assignment One, journaling your history, take your time with exploring the damage, and work at a safe pace for you; of course, by 'safe pace' we speak of emotional safety as well as physical safety. If the assignment becomes overwhelming – STOP, take a break. This is not a race to see how fast you can get through it. Discuss any struggles that are provoked either with your sponsor or counselor, or both. These ventures in discovery are not to be events that cause you to be re-traumatized.

Assignment Three - Living Amends

Assignments One and Two of Principle Five led you through a process of identifying those you've harmed and creating specific plans for making amends. Now, in Assignment Three, you have the opportunity to demonstrate real change. By taking action in making amends, you will show in overt ways the revolutions that are happening within your heart. For those around you, it may be the first clear example of your "walking the walk" of transformation.

MAKING SPECIFIC AMENDS

This assignment will consider two broad ways of making amends. First, we'll examine taking **specific actions**, whether directly or indirectly, of making restitution. Making **indirect amends** is the less complicated of the two. After getting feedback from your group, simply take the action. Do it quietly, without fanfare or attempts to draw attention to yourself.

Making **direct amends** is more risky. Be aware of these **guidelines** about your conversation with someone you've harmed:

- State the reason you want to talk to this person. Remember, you've probably hurt this individual in some deep way, and he or she may be wary about talking with you. If you make a specific appointment to meet, explain then (when you make the appointment) why you want to talk. If you haven't contacted someone on your list, but God provides an unexpected opportunity for an impromptu conversation, state in the beginning your desire to express your sorrow at the harm you've caused.
- Then state clearly how you've hurt this person. Be specific. General apologies are lame and may be perceived as insincere or an attempt to manipulate to get back into their good graces, which then has the potential for greater harm. Instead of saying, "I'm sorry I hurt you," say "I know it was painful when I forgot your birthday because I was absorbed in myself and my addiction. I'm sorry and I apologize." Be sure to say the actual words, *"I'm sorry and I apologize."* The mind-set of remorse is too important to let it be merely understood. I believe it's better to avoid asking for forgiveness. It's too easy to be manipulative with a request for forgiveness. If the person extends forgiveness, that's great. But that choice is theirs to make and should be made freely without prompting from you. Simply express your sorrow for the pain

you've caused and let go of the outcome. You are powerless over the person's reaction.

- Explain your intention to behave differently and any plan of restitution you'd like to make for the harm you've caused this person. Again, be specific about what you'd like to do to right the wrong.
- Listen to the individual's reaction. He or she may express anger or hurt at what you've done. Be patient and non-defensive. Agree with the harm you've caused and be empathetic to the person's pain.
- Thank the person for listening to your apology and for expressing his or her thoughts or feelings.

Don't expect any certain reaction or outcome when you try to make specific amends. Some people won't understand what you're doing and may brush you off. Others may still be too angry to hear you out. Perhaps more will accept your apology. The individual's reaction isn't the issue. *Your willingness to humbly accept responsibility for your behavior is the key point.* Remember the teaching in I Peter 5: 6: "Humble yourselves … under God's mighty hand, that He may lift you up in due time." Making amends is as much for you as it is for those you've harmed. It further releases your burden of shame and deepens your trust in God to take care of the outcome when you submit your will to Him.

Practicing Living Amends

The life-long challenge and task of recovery is to live differently in all areas of your life. By thought, word, and deed, an addict must daily observe the principles of focusing on healthiness and wholeness. In recovery terms, this kind of practice is called "living amends." In every situation you make the decisions, to the best of your ability, which are beneficial instead of harmful.

A first area of practicing living amends is obviously in maintaining sobriety. Without having integrity in how we manage our feelings in healthy ways rather than harming self or others, no other progress is possible. (This concept will be discussed at length in Principle Six) Remember the caution that was part of the final assignment of Principle One: The period of time during your second six months of sobriety is a dangerous time for relapse. It's easy to become lax about our recovery efforts as we become comfortable with our new lifestyle; we may let our guard down with an attitude like "I've got this whipped now." I want to remind you of one important tool of working your program: *boundaries remain crucial to your sobriety.* Review your work on boundaries from Principle One. Don't let your guard down!

A second major part of practicing living amends is following the Golden Rule: treating others the way you'd like to be treated. This requires a lot of maturity and self-sacrifice. It doesn't come naturally, especially to addicts who have a long history of focusing on their own gratification. A key way this concept relates to Principle Five is in learning to forgive others in exactly the same way you would like them to forgive you when you offer your amends.

Your work this far through this text and with your L.I.F.E. Recovery Group has put you in touch with some profound areas of your own woundedness. You've identified ways you've been deeply hurt by others, perhaps even by some in your own family. You've allowed yourself to feel your feelings of loss, grief, hurt, anger, sadness, and loneliness. You understand the ways you've been abused or abandoned.

Principle Five challenges you to forgive those who have harmed you, as well as to humbly make amends to those you have harmed. For some of us, this undertaking is more difficult. Maybe you'd like to nurse your resentments a little longer. Perhaps you've become comfortable in your victim role. Holding on to a grudge lets you ignore any part you may have contributed to the relationship problems.

A clear sign of a changed life course is that you're willing to let go of the dues others owe you. Whether or not the offender expresses sorrow at the pain he or she has caused, you choose to forgive (to let go of the dues others owe you just as God has let go of the debt owed to Him) and move forward. You allow God to be the judge and the punisher for wrongs. Paul issues this challenge:

> *"Do not repay anyone evil for evil.... If it is possible, as far as it depends on you, live at peace with everyone. Do not take revenge, my friends, but leave room for God's wrath, for it is written, 'It is mine to avenge; I will repay,' says the Lord. On the contrary: 'If your enemy is hungry, feed; if he is thirsty, give something to drink.... Do not be overcome by evil, but overcome evil with good."* (Romans 12:17-21)

Don't be discouraged by how difficult it is to make amends to others and to extend grace to others. This will be a life-long process as you grow in your relationship with a forgiving God. You won't do either of these recovery tasks perfectly. Sometimes you won't have the maturity or judgment to even try. Because you're human, you will continue to cause harm occasionally.

Remember our Lord's promise: *"My grace is sufficient for you, for my power is made perfect in weakness."* (2 Corinthians 12: 9)

Journaling Exercise: Your Tasks

Take two specific actions:

> 1. *Make one direct amend to someone you've harmed*
> 2. *Make one form of indirect amend*

Record what you did in your journal, along with how you felt. Be prepared to share your actions and feelings with your L.I.F.E. Recovery Group.

Journaling Exercise: Forgiving

Share the names and situations with your sponsor. *Pray together for willingness and help in letting go of your right to avenge the wrongs you've suffered. You may not be able to forgive in person, but you can still do it in your heart and mind.*	***Five People I Need to Forgive:*** 1. _____ 2. _____ 3. _____ 4. _____ 5. _____

Ask your group for affirmations about how far you've come in your journey to *Live In Freedom Everyday.*

PRINCIPLE SIX
Assignment Three – Growing Spiritually

In fellowship with others we develop honest relationships, where we celebrate our progress and continue to address our weaknesses.

Living in Fellowship: I Cannot Succeed Alone

Congratulations for having come this far in your journey to maintain sobriety and wholesome integrity. It has taken courage, perseverance, and commitment. In many ways it may have been harder than you anticipated. Some may have considered giving up, but you have persevered, and here you are. You've experienced many feelings that have been painful for you: the old, familiar feelings which you have worked so hard in the past to escape. Now you are learning that, with the help of others of similar experience, you are able to work your way through the pain, stress and urgency without medicating. You may have experienced feelings new to you. You've humbled yourself in admitting the full truth about your history, your thoughts, feelings, and acting out behaviors. With God's help, you've made progress on a long journey. You've told the story of your road to addiction and the acting out behaviors in which you have engaged, and the life history that has generated the pain for which you have sought relief. You've decided that you want to get well and that the ways in which you have sought relief have not worked; and you have surrendered your life to Christ. You have begun to identify the wounds you have suffered that have been the source of your pain and the people who have inflicted these wounds, and have begun the process of forgiveness that will set you free from the bondage of your pain. Christ Jesus is the Power and the Strength that has gotten, and will continue to get you through. You've accepted accountability from a sponsor, and perhaps have begun working with a counselor. You have begun identifying those you have harmed by your behavior, and are willing to make amends to those you have harmed. I pray you're beginning to have a deeper sense of God's power and presence in your life.

Principle Six guides you into a way of living that involves genuine connection with others, instead of the isolation you've probably known. The foundation for this work comes from the following principle:

Fellowship is equal to freedom from fear.

It's probably hard for you to believe this promise since you may have been isolated for years as you've hidden your addiction from others, and have experienced the pain of relationships in which trust has not been present. You've never known the joy of a supportive community. Your shame has kept you from connecting with others, while it continued to fuel your craving for the acting out behavior of choice which produced the illusion of relief. (You also probably can't imagine a life free from your 'drug of choice,' the behaviors that produced the excitement of your addiction, which has felt like your constant companion for as long as you can remember.) Principle Six offers a path out of your isolation which, in turn, is the road to sobriety and wholesome integrity in a new lifestyle.

Hopefully, you're already enjoying some of the benefits of such fellowship through your L.I.F.E. Recovery Group. You're bonding with other Christians who have faced similar struggles and seek to live in sobriety and freedom. You're beginning to experience both the grace of God, and the grace from other Christians who will love you despite your mistakes.

Assignment Three – Growing Spiritually

The main activity of this assignment is a matter of "**conversion.**" No, it's probably not what you're thinking. I don't mean the religious kind of conversion that changes a person from a non-Christian to a Christian or from one Christian denomination to another. You've hopefully already done that and you have found a Christian fellowship with which you have united and are actively engaged. The conversion I'm proposing is about converting all the energy you used to pursue your *addiction* into energy that you use to pursue *God*.

You know, of course, that the key to this conversion will be **discipline** – a discipline necessary to make ongoing change in your life. Note how the word "discipline" is from the same root word as "disciple." This word means to be a "learner" who is a follower of a teacher. In the Bible, persons who wished to become teachers would be tutored by a rabbi; they would become followers of a particular rabbi (such as the Apostle Paul who, as Saul, had been a disciple of Gamaliel). The word also refers to practice and correction. Does the description of being a follower and a learner fit you? Are you open to correction? Do you "practice" the tenets of your faith? If so, you must be a person of discipline.

I know for certain that you already have *some* of the characteristics of a disciple. For example, you have the *energy* to follow Christ. Think again of how much energy you spent being a follower in pursuit of your "next high." If you can't seem to find the energy for a spiritual walk, you may be experiencing some level of shame and depression.

You also have the capacity to *practice* to follow Christ. Do you remember the category of ritual in the cycle of addiction? Your ritual was something you practiced a lot! Ritual isn't a bad word; it can be a spiritual one. In fact, you'll need rituals to pursue your spiritual path. For this assignment you'll also need "**enthusiasm.**" Enthusiasm is a Greek word that literally means "God (Theos) is in us." *God is in you.* Do you believe that?

Read the entire fifteenth chapter of the Gospel of John. Jesus says that He will be in you if you are in Him. He says a lot of other things, doesn't He? He describes the vine and the branches and how the Master Gardner prunes the branches that don't produce fruit. Are you feeling rather pruned? As you learn to abide in Christ, you'll draw nourishment from Him, and you'll bear more fruit.

In Assignment One of Principle Six, you started keeping a daily inventory. One of the categories you were asked to assess was spirituality. In this assignment, I want you to be much more aggressive in your thinking about this area.

Sometimes when we think about spiritual discipline, we mean that we need to have a "quiet time." My experience suggests that many addicts aren't very good at that practice. We're impatient by nature, and we don't like doing anything "quietly." For the restless among us, increasing our spirituality may be a matter of doing something more active, such as going somewhere to participate in Bible study or corporate prayer or corporate meditation. It may mean going to concerts or Christian seminars. It may be putting a cassette or CD into your car stereo and listening to praise music or inspirational teaching while you're driving (we addicts like to multi-task). There are also many different kinds of workbooks that might help you grow in spiritual discipline. I think of Henry Blackaby's *Experiencing God*, for example. Be creative in planning how you can better connect with God, just as you were creative in your addiction.

Another way of describing what we're after is "**quest**." We're on a religious quest to get closer to God. For some, the quest may involve many active behaviors designed to help find Him. I have known men, for example, who actually travel to places of religious significance, like the Holy Land, as a way of "experiencing God." This kind of quest may not be something that many of you can afford, but it's an example of something active. A spiritual retreat or dedicated time away from your daily responsibilities is another activity that could be part of a spiritual quest.

For some of us, discipline or quest may mean doing some act of service. It could be working in the soup kitchen, volunteering at church, visiting in the nursing home, or planning a mission trip. We might volunteer for work or participate in a church activity. We might teach a Sunday School class (there's nothing quite like teaching to help you study for yourself).

Are you getting the idea? To be spiritually disciplined, you need to *do* something. It will probably be something you've never done before – perhaps even a practice far outside your comfort zone. You may need encouragement to get it done, which you can request from your L.I.F.E. Recovery Group.

In some church traditions there's a role for "spiritual director," who is one who directs your prayer life, Bible study, and meditations. Has there ever been such a person in your life? In this recovery program, you might originally think of your sponsor as one who directs you in spiritual discipline. In this assignment, you may want to think of another person who can fill this role.

I encourage you to think "outside the box." Your spiritual director may not be from your own tradition or denomination. The key to this role of "spiritual director" is to hold you accountable to those things that you have agreed to do. Your pastor may suggest some people in your church who are willing to take on such a role.

Maybe you don't have a regular church where you attend. It could be time to "shop" for one until you discover the fellowship where you feel accepted, comfortable, and challenged.
Finally, here is one last thought. In John 15, Jesus says that there is no greater gift than to lay down your life for another. Addicts are terrible at practicing self-sacrifice. *Our addiction*

has been selfish. As we grow in spirituality, we'll be transformed into *selflessness.* Think about the theme of sacrifice as you consider what you should do to have more discipline. Whatever the activity, it should involve some sacrifice of your time, energy, resources, or money.

Journaling Exercise: Growing in Spirituality

1. *Write the name of a person(s) who will hold you accountable to having more spiritual discipline in your life.*

2. *What is one act of service you're willing to do?*

3. *Name a section of Scripture you commit to studying.*

4. *Who is a spiritual teacher you enjoy? What books are you reading or tapes are you listening to?*

5. *What is your favorite kind of spiritual music?*

6. *If you're participating in a Bible study or similar class, note that.*

7. *Have you attended any workshops or seminars recently?*

8. *Where are you attending worship services? Does this church feel like home? Why or why not?*

These are just some suggestions to help you begin practicing spiritual disciplines. Remember, there's no such thing as the perfect spiritual program. This growth is a journey for life. If you've accepted Christ as your savior, you've already received salvation, so spiritual discipline isn't about your effort to win favor with God. It's about your time with God and your attempt to know Him more intimately.

God's blessings to you in this quest.

PRINCIPLE SEVEN
Assignment Three: Discovering Your Vision

Having experienced healing from trauma, woundedness, and awakening in our spirit as the result of our work in transformation, we will strive to carry the message of Christ's healing power to those who still struggle, and we pursue a vision of God's purpose for our lives.

Finding a Purpose: I Have a Vision

Scripture reminds us "where there is no vision, the people perish." (Proverbs 29:18 KJV) This speaks for individuals as well as for nations. It is tragic the number of people who have no vision for their life, no purpose to fulfill, no thought for tomorrow, no hope for tomorrow. We are likely to ask, "Why on earth did I do everything I did?" "What was God's purpose for my life?" "How did I get so off track from God's purpose?" There are no easy answers to these questions but understand this:

You cannot undo what is done,
and
You must go forward from here.

As you work through our last principle you will learn how to go forward and use what you are doing now to carry the message of Christ's healing to those who still suffer. Just like in Luke 22:32 where Jesus speaks to Peter, *"When you have turned, strengthen your brother."*

In the first assignment you will prepare your story, which will become your testimony. You will begin sharing your testimony in the second assignment, first with your trusted L.I.F.E. Recovery Group, then, as you become stronger, with others. When you work on the third assignment you will be developing your Vision, your "Mission Statement" for how you want to conduct your life.

Developing your addiction story is foundational to determining what is next and answering the following questions: What will my life look like in the future? My dreams, desires, aspirations for the time that remains of my life? Answers to these three questions will unfold over the next 14 weeks in the form of your recovery story, where you started and where you will go all enveloped in the work to be done in Assignments Two and Three for Principle Seven.

Assignment Three: Discovering Your Vision

Having vision is a familiar biblical concept. Both the Old and New Testaments recount the stories of countless people who acted according to divine vision. Today, a "vision" is a popular term to describe an inspiring or motivating mental image of the future.

In Assignment Three, you'll work on having that kind of positive mental image of where God wants you to go. Do you remember the earlier work around understanding your fantasies that was part of Principle One? I expressed my hope that you'd be able to replace the fantasies in your life with a vision.

Here's the comparison:

*A fantasy is an image of a preferred future
in which all of your wounds are healed.*

∞

*A vision is an image of a preferred future
in which you pursue God's plan for your life.*

From your work in Assignment Two of this Principle, "Sharing Your Pain," you saw how your wounds can be your guides, your teachers that connect you with God and with others. Your wounds may also become your strengths, in that you're a stronger person for having gone through your experiences in life.

The first task of this assignment is to figure out how you become a person of vision.

First, you must discover and accept your true gifts. You might be surprised to find that for years you've been pursuing what others, such as your parents, identified as your gifts. They may or may not have had your best interests at heart. Reflect on the messages your family gave you about what you were supposed to do in life. My father, for example, never actually told me to be a minister, but he so valued that role that all of his modeling and encouragement was in that direction. Since part of my job was to take care of him, it was also apparent that I was to have care-giving skills. In order to please him, I think, I went into ministry. Don't get me wrong, I now believe that I am truly called to ministry, but it is something I had to claim for myself, not something to do to please Dad.

Think of your family's messages, their modeling and values. How were you encouraged or discouraged? What was your role(s) in your family? Were some jobs or careers valued more than others?

Journaling Exercise: Your Family's Mission for You

> *Write the "mission statement" you internalized from your family.*

For example, my mission statement would be simple: "Become a minister and take care of everyone else and not yourself."

It is possible for others to encourage you about your true gifts. First, think of those people in your life who were truly affirming and positive. Maybe it was a teacher, a coach, a pastor, or a friend. These supporters believed in you and encouraged your interests. What skills, talents, and abilities did they affirm in you?

Journaling Exercise: Your Encouragers

Write the names of supportive people and their affirmations:

_____   _____

_____   _____

_____   _____

_____   _____

Now, reflect on those times when you've felt truly passionate about what you were doing. These will be times when you're "in the zone" and are certain you're doing exactly the right thing. What do you relish? What brings you a sense of fulfillment? What do you do that lights others' faces with joy? For what things have others thanked you?

Journaling Exercise: Your Passions

Describe some of the times you felt passionate, energetic, and fulfilled. What were you doing? How did others respond? What were the results?

Next, reflect on your education and your life experiences. What's been your training? What jobs have you held? What volunteer work have you done? Do you have hobbies? Have you been involved with sports?

Journaling Exercise: Your Experience

Prepare or review your "resume" of education, employment, hobbies, and critical life experiences.

Finally, and this is a hard one, reflect again on what you've learned through painful experiences in your life, including the ones related to your coping methods and dependencies. Pain can be a great teacher and guide. God often speaks through hardship. James 1:2 says, *"Count it all joy when you experience various trials, for you know that the testing of your faith produces steadfastness."*

Journaling Exercise: Your Lessons

> **Make a list of all the lessons you've learned through your own pain. Remember, this pain could be about loss, failure, hardship, or crisis.**

You now have several lists and sets of reflections. Read back over them until a picture emerges of your true gifts.

If you've never seen the movie, "The Chariots of Fire," you might want to rent it. It's a wonderful comparison of two men who pursue their gifts and talents for two different reasons. The main characters in this true story are Eric Liddel and Harold Abrahams, who each are preparing for the 1924 Olympic Games. Both are fast and gifted runners. They're the best in the United Kingdom in the hundred-meter dash, and they both have a dream of winning the Olympic gold medal.

Harold Abrahams is the son of a Jewish businessman. He knows his family has never been fully accepted in English society, and he longs to be accepted. The pain of ethnic prejudice burns inside him and fuels his anger. He concludes that the way to be accepted is to be the world's fastest man and to "run all of his opponents into the ground." He even hires a coach and trains incessantly. Harold Abrahams does win the gold medal in the hundred-meter dash, but the end of the movie shows that it doesn't bring joy. The accomplishment he'd dreamed about is almost a disappointment.

Eric Liddel is the son of missionaries to China. He's back in Scotland studying to be in ministry and to go back to China as a missionary. Eric Liddel knows that his athletic gift is from God. His sister, though, grows concerned that his athletic training for the Olympics is distracting him from his "true" work of studying and preparing to return to China. In a powerful scene, Eric takes his sister out on the hills overlooking Edinburgh, Scotland, and he says, "Jenny, I know that the Lord made me for China, but He also made me fast. *And when I run, I feel God's pleasure.*"

During the Olympic games, Eric Liddel refuses to run the hundred-meter dash because one of the qualifying races is scheduled on a Sunday. He switches to the four hundred-meter dash, instead, and he wins the gold medal. He's elated and knows a true sense of joy.

An interesting detail accurately depicted in "Chariots of Fire" is Eric's unusual running style. In the middle of the race, he would throw back his head and close his eyes. He literally couldn't see where he was going. Eric was a man running with God's help. He understood that when God was in control, he didn't need to see where he was going.

170

What are you doing when you feel God's pleasure - when you don't need to see where you're going? Bill Hybels, of Willow Creek Church, says that Christians will know they hear the voice of the Holy Spirit by the joy and excitement they feel about what they're thinking or doing.

Journaling Exercise: God's Pleasure

Make a list of times when you've felt that you were doing something that brought you pure joy – when you could feel "God's pleasure."

You now have some lists to think and pray about. They encompass your own perception and the perception of others about your talents and gifts. How does this information match up with the expectations you brought from your family of origin? How does it match with what you're currently doing? Don't just think about these questions vocationally, but in the totality of your life.

Consider your work in Principle Four around developing character traits, which was based on the fruits of the Spirit described in Galatians 5. What do you think determines character? Is it a matter of pure will power, or is it a matter of **vision**? Think about it this way. You know that your fantasy life drove your behaviors for years, which led you into traits of character that resulted in despair *Fantasy is actually a form of a vision*, because it's a mental image of an outcome you desire. If that kind of vision is capable of driving behavior and of driving character, wouldn't you also think that a godly vision would drive behavior and character?

My friend and colleague in ministry, Eli Machen, is fond of talking about buzzards. Much to our distaste, buzzards have a huge appetite for dead animals. God made them that way. He also gave them the sight (or vision capability) to see dead animals miles away from hundreds of feet in the air. Because of their vision, these birds can fly around and see things that we don't see. *Buzzards have a buzzard's character and behavior.* And they teach us an important lesson:

Appetite can drive a vision.

What is your appetite? Remember the story of Jesus' encounter with the woman at the well of Samaria. She was thirsty for "living water," but she confused it with relationships with men. Her "appetite" for connecting with men drove her into five marriages and a sixth relationship with a live-in partner.

What, again, are you thirsty for? In your old life, you were thirsty for the relief you found in your addiction. Spiritually, however, we also have an appetite for God. Our problem with alcohol/drug, gambling, sex, or other means to medicate our emotional pain is that we've confused these two appetites. <u>We've replaced our appetite for God with our appetite for the world's answer to our distress.</u> The great English writer G.K. Chesterson wrote, "A man who knocks at the door of a brothel is looking for God."

We've been thirsty for love, nurture, touch, affirmation, acceptance, and fellowship. We've thought that we could get these normal desires met through our addiction, but we've been wrong. (For some of us, nearly dead wrong!) We can only get these things from God. This confused appetite has driven our character and our behavior: We've had addictive behaviors born from a flawed character created by a faulty appetite. It's time to get reoriented.

Vision pursues an appetite for God's best interest. If you allow yourself to see that truth, it will drive your character and your behavior. It will form your discipline.

Imagine what it would be like to pursue God with the same energy you've pursued your addiction.

The next step in understanding your vision is to understand the legacy you hope to create. A legacy is how you'll be remembered and the influence you'll leave on others after you die. Here are some questions to consider, assuming you die before some important people in your life:

1. How would you like your spouse to remember you? What will he or she say about you after you're gone?
2. How also would you like your children to remember you? What will they say about you at future family gatherings? What stories will they tell about you, your character, and your behavior?
3. Who else will remember you when you die? Who'll want to attend your funeral and why will they want to be there? What will be said at your memorial service? What will be highlighted in your obituary?
4. What contributions and acts of service will you be remembered for?

Journal your answers to the questions above. Humbly ask God to show you the truth about your current legacy. If you doubt your ability to see yourself clearly, ask a trusted friend to share their honest impressions.

This is your legacy.

Journaling Exercise: Your Legacy

Tough questions, aren't they? I suggest that if you can answer them courageously, you'll have a vision of what your true heart desires. Strangely enough, I believe it will be consistent with what God desires for you, too.

When you've worked through all of the suggested writing exercises, you're ready for the last part of this assignment: articulating your personal vision.

Journaling Exercise: Your Vision

As an example, here is mine: "I am to write, teach, speak, and counsel for the purpose of educating the Church about mental and spiritual health and integrity." This brief statement incorporates my gifts, talents, and passion, and expresses what brings me joy. It also describes what I'd like to be remembered for after I'm gone.

Men and women of integrity are men and women of vision. They know where they're going and what they want to do. They follow their passions with purity and fervor. If you continue to develop and honor your vision, you'll find that your behaviors will follow. Remember, again, how addiction behaviors followed your fantasies. As you're transformed into the man or woman God intends you to be, your vision will direct your decisions.

Before you finish, go back and look at the healthy cycle I created that's presented in Principle Six, Assignment Two. It shows the progression from connection with God and His family to vision, to healthy disciplines, to healthy choices, to joy. My guess is that you've changed a great deal already. My expectation is that the integrity of your behavior blesses you with serenity and joy. And my ongoing prayer is that you'll continue to grow in strength and faith as you allow God to transform you into someone who lives in freedom every day.

Tying It All Together: Transformation Principles from Nehemiah

For this section we will need warriors. The work of understanding these principles is not for cowards. It is for those who are willing to take risks.

Before you have a shame attack concerning your lack of courage, remember that you have been given all that you need by God. Your job is to find it. It might be as simple as deciding to act courageously.

A reporter once asked a famous British general during the era of the great empire under Queen Victoria, "Why is the British soldier so much braver than others?" His reply was fascinating. He said, "The British soldier is not braver than our enemies; he is simply braver one minute longer."

Are you willing to be braver one minute longer? AA says that we should take it one day at a time. Are you willing to be brave today?

If you are, decide to tackle the material in the book of Nehemiah, which contains a blueprint for accountability. Your job is to seek God's wisdom about how He would have you act responsibly and courageously to defend against the attacks of Satan that would seek to defeat your sobriety.

The book of Nehemiah is perhaps less familiar and less frequently studied than many of the other books of the Old Testament. To overlook this book, however, is to miss some of the richest material in the Bible. The teaching hidden in Nehemiah is highly applicable to our journey of living in freedom every day. Indeed, it's a great summary of much of this entire *L.I.F.E. Recovery Guide*. Your L.I.F.E. Recovery Group may want to discuss one of these principles at every meeting, or at least at selected meetings.

The story of Nehemiah takes place during a time when the Babylonians had defeated Israel. The city of Jerusalem and the temple of God had been destroyed. Many Jews had been taken back to Babylon to work as slaves. Nehemiah was one of these captives. He apparently had distinguished himself as responsible and trustworthy, because he'd been given an important job: the cupbearer to the Babylonian king, Artaxerxes. The cupbearer was required to taste all of the king's food and drink to make sure that someone wasn't trying to poison the king. It was a potentially dangerous job, but at least Nehemiah's living conditions were vastly superior to his fellow slaves. He got to hang out with the king in the throne room and partake of the finest food in the land. Yet Nehemiah was constantly mindful of his dependence on God and of the devastation of God's holy land.

With this background in mind, consider the following principles from the book of Nehemiah. These 18 principles tie together the process of transformation which is outlined in this *L.I.F.E. Recovery Guide*.

NEHEMIAH: TRANSFORMATION PRINCIPLES

1. Accountability begins with humility.
2. Accountability depends on honest confession about your situation.
3. Accountability involves asking for help and stating your needs.
4. The journey of healing is never traveled alone. You will need the army around you.
5. The process of accountability assumes that the enemy wants to defeat us, especially when we start trying to do the right thing.
6. In the face of overwhelming damage and discouragement, rebuilding may be a matter of just getting started.
7. Being transformed requires getting the garbage out of your life.
8. Transformation begins at home.
9. Transformation requires preparing ahead of time for the attacks that will come.
10. Transformation means guarding the weakest places where you're most vulnerable.
11. Accountability is always with a group, not just with one person.
12. Our motivation for transformation should be selfless.
13. Transformation means building as well as defending.
14. Transformation means putting positive things into your life.
15. Transformation is an ongoing, lifelong process, but God provides sustaining energy.
16. When tempted, remain committed to transformation without wavering.
17. Transformation targets you for rumors and personal attacks.
18. Transformation results in a willingness to sacrifice even your own life

---

Nehemiah Principle One:
Accountability begins with humility.

In the beginning of the book, one of Nehemiah's brothers, Hanani, comes with other men to tell about the destruction of Jerusalem. You might expect that if Nehemiah were to be a great leader, he'd jump up with a plan to do something about this problem. As you read the story, however, you see that when he heard this news, Nehemiah sat down and wept (Neh. 1:4).
In Principle Two of the seven principles of L.I.F.E., you were challenged about your willingness to find sobriety from addiction and sin. Willingness is about humility. It's about knowing that we can't control our own lives. It's about knowing that we need God. Nehemiah is humble with a humility that comes from his great sadness.

You, also, may find humility in your sadness as you consider the destructive nature of your sins. Sadness over your current state is the beginning of transformation. Humility reminds you that you can only get well with the help of God. Those who are broken know they need help. Accountability can only begin when we know that we need help and that we can't do it alone. The basic lesson from the first chapter of Nehemiah is that if you aren't willing to depend on God instead of relying on yourself, you won't find healing.

The rest of chapter one is Nehemiah's prayer to God. He first confesses that the Jews have behaved wickedly. (Remember the work you completed in Principle Three about confession.) The second part of the prayer asks God to restore the Jews to their home. Confessional prayer is the first response of a humble heart. After your confession of humility, ask God to restore you by His grace.

Nehemiah Principle Two:
Accountability depends on honest confession about your situation and repentance.

In the opening of chapter two, Nehemiah still doesn't have a plan. He is still sad. The king, who apparently was quite discerning, asks Nehemiah why he looks so sad and then gives his own diagnosis, recognizing, *"This can only be sadness of heart."* Nehemiah honestly replies, *"Why shouldn't I look so sad when the city where my fathers are buried lies in ruins and its gates have been destroyed by fire?"* (Neh. 2:4) The account continues with Nehemiah's admission, *"I was very much afraid."*

Our journey begins when we honestly admit the condition of our lives. As long as we hide our situation and deny our feelings, we'll remain captives of the enemy. In my experience, what we are not so good at in the church is having opportunities to confess to spiritual authority. I'm not talking about some printed confession in the Sunday bulletin. No, face to face confession, I believe, is much more important. We learn a lot about confession and willingness to ask for help in our families. When we think we don't need help, we often lie to others who ask us how we are doing and we say, "fine," for most of us, most of the time that's just not true. When we don't share our feelings with those we love and those we want to be in relationship with, it keeps us isolated and even distant. This isolation creates loneliness, a feeling that most of us really don't like talking about. The bottom line is how can we be accountable to anyone or any group if we don't know how to share our feelings? Along with confession is repentance, Nehemiah in 1:8-9 reminds God of a promise that if the Jewish people will return to God and obey God's commandments, God will return them to their home even if they are scattered to the farthest corner of the earth.

Nehemiah Principle Three
Accountability involves asking for help and stating your needs.

The king surprises Nehemiah by responding with an unexpected question: "What is it you want?" Despite his fear, Nehemiah dares to ask the king's help. (Notice that he prays first and prefaces his request with a compliment for the king.) Then, perhaps even more surprising than the king's question is his answer to Nehemiah's request: The king says "yes." So, Nehemiah gets to go home. When you confront your fears, ask for help, and clearly state your needs, you may be surprised at the result.

When we think about it the word "need" is often used when we really mean the word "should." It is common for many to say, "I need to pray more," or "I need to make more calls to those in group." Those are not "needs;" they are "shoulds." Expressing a need is really asking for help. We all have rather large and universal needs. Years ago my wife and I asked ourselves what needs God created inside all of us. We knew that God created "male and female" in "his own image" (Gen. 1:27). Since men and women are made in God's image, we felt they must have many things in common. So believing that men and women have the same universal needs, we also felt that many of us don't always get those needs met as we grow up and that we learn to cope with that lack of fulfillment.

If you are going to be accountable, in order to do so, you should know what the big needs or desires are. As I list them, try to think about your own life. Ask yourself how well you did about getting them met in childhood and later in life. If you didn't get them met, ask yourself how you learned to cope with that.

Our universal needs are:

To be heard and understood,
affirmed, blessed, safe, touched, chosen and included.

Nehemiah Principle Four
The journey of healing is never traveled alone.
You will need the army around you.

Nehemiah asks also for some letters of reference that will give safe passage through the territories on the way to Jerusalem. With those letters in hand, he's ready to go. Nehemiah plans to travel alone almost 1,000 miles through territory occupied by many enemies of the Jews. But the king is wiser, and he keeps Nehemiah from making one of the great mistakes that many of us also make. We frequently imitate Nehemiah, who thought he could take this enormous journey alone. The king, however, sent army officers and cavalry to accompany Nehemiah (chapter 2, verse 9). Remember, you must not attempt a journey of transformation alone. Our "army" can be found in our L.I.F.E. Recovery Group. These are men or women who are willing to stand with us against the attack. I've never known anyone who has changed a negative behavior on his or her own or even with the help of only one accountability partner. You must be willing to go to any length, geographically, emotionally and logically to find your "army officers and cavalry."

Nehemiah Principle Five
Accountability assumes that the enemy wants to defeat us,
especially when we start trying to do the right thing.

In verse 10 of chapter two, it's clear that the enemies of Israel don't like any thought of rebuilding projects. There are vital analogies throughout this book, and this is an important one. So many Christians assume that when they start a healing process and seek to return to the Lord, their lives will automatically get better. We may think we'll be spared the consequences of our behavior because we've committed to change. We hope our new way of life erases the results of the old. This passage from Nehemiah reminds us that Satan hates our intention to do the right thing and to rebuild. In I Peter 5:8, Peter compares Satan to a lion roaming around and waiting to devour his prey. Nehemiah's journey home is symbolic of our journey when we want to return to our home in God. Satan doesn't want us to make that journey. He is going to attack us. Satan knows the places in our lives where we are most vulnerable. He has countless forms and tells innumerable lies.

Nehemiah Principle Six
In the face of overwhelming discouragement and damage, rebuilding may simply be a matter of just getting started.

When Nehemiah gets home to Jerusalem, the end of chapter two describes that he goes out at night to survey the damage. It must have been like looking at Ground Zero after the World Trade Center was destroyed by terrorists. What a terrible sight! The analogy here is that for many of us who seek healing, we might suddenly wake up to all the damage we've created around us. This realization can be extremely discouraging. The enormity of the rebuilding task can be daunting. We may feel paralyzed and not know how or where to start to rebuild. In AA language, Nehemiah does "the next right thing." He simply gathers everyone and non-dramatically says, "Let's start rebuilding."

(At the end of chapter two the enemies present themselves again. Nehemiah reminds everyone that God is in control and that they belong to Him. He says that the enemies have no historic claim to the people of God. In like fashion, when you're under attack, remind yourself that Satan has no claim on your life if you're a believer in Christ.)

The next section is an outline of the specific way Nehemiah starts his enormous job. Chapter three, on the surface, is a hard one with its long list of difficult names. However, the chapter is a wonderful example of organization. Nehemiah divides the work into small segments and various groups accept responsibility for each piece.

The division of labor outlined in Nehemiah Three isn't a unique principle. This age-old wisdom reminds us that if we look at the whole project of pursuing recovery, we may feel overwhelmed. But when we simply start building and focus on the immediate task at hand, we ultimately will reach our goal. The great AA phrase "one day at a time" certainly applies. Despite the damage and the discouragement, the first step of transformation is to simply get started.

Nehemiah Principle Seven
Accountability requires getting the garbage out of your life.

Hidden in the verses of chapter three are two great principles. Verse 14 reports that Malkijah repairs the Dung Gate. (That term is the NIV translation. Substitute your own word - garbage, manure, or whatever suits you). Jerusalem had many gates and each one had a function. Obviously, the Dung Gate was the gate that channeled the garbage and refuse out of the city. It was the sanitation gate, which was vital or else the city would choke on its own filth. If you've ever been in a city that was having a garbage strike, you'll understand the importance of the Dung Gate. Many health experts believe that the greatest advance of the 20th century was the widespread use of sanitation. This modern practice is responsible for ridding the world of more filth and disease than any other medical advance.

One analogy applicable here is that you might feel sometimes that your lot in life has involved dealing with dung. You get the worst assignments, the unimportant tasks, etc. An important principle from Nehemiah is that sometimes what seems like the filthy project might be the most important one.

There's another important point about the Dung Gate: What is the filth in your life? What do you need to get rid of? Think about Paraphernalia Garbage, those contributing objects or materials involved with your coping. Let's first remember that you are trying to change a particular behavior. When you think about that behavior, ask yourself if there are any objects or materials that contribute to that behavior. For example, a smoker would have a lighter or ashtrays around the house. If you drink too much, get rid of the alcohol in your house, office or even in your car. Maybe you eat too much. Are there certain foods in your house you need to get rid of? Be relentless. Maybe it's to throw away a stash of pornography, remove Internet access from your computer, cancel cable service to your home, or say goodbye to an affair partner.

All behavior has a backstory – a series of events and circumstances that led up to it. In the field of addiction we call this series of events a ritual. All behaviors start with a thought about doing the behavior. The thought is usually triggered by some event, interaction, or stimulus. Perhaps it is a stressful event at work, an argument with a spouse, or a perceived rejection of some kind. We sometimes call these thoughts preoccupations, fantasies, or obsessions if we spend hours every day just thinking about the behavior.

Don't forget that there may be emotions you need to deal with as part of the garbage of your life. This "dung" could be anger, resentments, or jealousy. It could be deep hurts from old memories. These may take longer to work on, but don't ignore the feelings you need to deal with. Pride is garbage. Pride is about pain, fear and sadness. As we already know, garbage stinks and we need to get rid of it. This is really true when it comes to thoughts that pollute our brains. There are different types of "stinking thinking." Let's list several of them for you here: delusions, rationalizations and lies. So accountability will remind us that every behavior, object, excuse or lie that is a part of the ritual must also be stopped.

Nehemiah Principle Eight
Accountability means building close to home.

Look at verses 23 and 30 of chapter three and note that these people made repairs to the parts of the walls that were across from or next to their own houses. This is an important point. So many of us get into "global thinking" when we embrace the healing journey. We want to rush out and tell the world about the new and helpful things we're learning. Before recovery, many of us distract ourselves by helping others rather than addressing our own problems. The message of Nehemiah 3 is that we need to build close to home. Before we go off in haste to evangelize the world about recovery, we should repair the damage to our own homes, to our spouses, and to our children. "First things first" is another AA slogan, and the first rebuilding must happen at home. Before we go off too hastily, we should ask ourselves what repairs need to be made to our own homes, to our spouses and to our children.

Nehemiah Principle Nine
Accountability means preparing ahead of time for the attacks to come.

Chapter four is a vital chapter. It begins with a description of how the enemies are marshaling their energies to come against the building project. Nehemiah knows that the enemy is capable and deadly and that everyone needs to be prepared. Remember that the enemy in the story is a representation of how Satan attacks. The people could easily get discouraged by the threat. Nehemiah deals with the menace by praying and by posting a guard day and night (verse 9).

The message for recovery is clear: You can't wait for the attack to come. Instead, you must *prepare for it*. Living by this principle is a great challenge. So many men fall because they tell themselves, "When I get tempted, then I'll call someone or do something." That's your pride talking. When you get tempted, a part of the temptation is that you're lonely, angry, bored, and lustful. You probably won't feel like calling anyone then. You won't want to resist the temptation or deal with it. You may be into your juvenile feelings of entitlement and convince yourself that you "deserve" to get some of your needs met in a sinful way. *If you wait until you're in trouble before asking for help, you won't ask.* Let me state this principle another way:

We must prepare in a time of <u>strength</u> for the times of weakness that will surely come.

You must prepare for the attacks against your sobriety. When you are humble and convicted enough that you want to change and to be sober, put energy into fortifying your recovery plan. Consider specifically how you'll guard your heart and position others to stand with you for protection.

Reflect back on the work you did in Principle One about your rituals. Do you remember the lists you made of behaviors you'll have to stop in order to prevent yourself from getting into your rituals? Thinking through your rituals and setting boundaries is part of preparation. Again, let me be clear:

Don't wait for temptation! Prepare for it, because it will come.

Do you get the point? *What?* You think being in recovery means you've had brain surgery and all cravings have been removed? Did you think that the world has been transformed and all triggers have vanished? You think you're better than others who must work at being sober? Get humble and get prepared.

Nehemiah Principle Ten
Accountability means guarding the weakest places where you're most vulnerable.

Nehemiah chapter four describes another important strategy that applies to recovery: Not only is the guard positioned day and night, but it's also placed at the weakest places. You must be sure you have warriors standing with you in your most vulnerable places.
This isn't rocket science. Know your weak places (selfishness, tiredness and boredom) ask your accountability group to remind you to "work your program." Weaknesses can be thought of in several categories, ritual weakness, emotional weakness, spiritual weakness, physical weakness, triggers and ADHD. When you know your weaknesses and rituals and how you get most sorely tempted, make sure a number of people in your group are aware of those pitfalls. Ask them to help you prepare for those times, so that you have automatic defenses in place. How can defense happen automatically? One basic example is to call someone from your L.I.F.E. Recovery Group every day. Schedule times during the day when you know you'll talk to someone. And don't depend on your willingness to make a call. Ask them to call you if they don't hear from you by a certain time.

If during your call you practice expressing your feelings and processing any pain that has come up you will quickly strengthen your relational and intimacy skills. In another example, if you travel, a good plan for preparing upfront for possible temptations is to make sure several people know your schedule and where you're going. Arrange with them to call you at various times so that you can expect to hear from someone and not get yourself into trouble. Do you see how this strategy works?

During your L.I.F.E. Recovery Group meeting, share your weakest places of vulnerability. Ask your group to help you construct a plan that's proactive in providing defenses. Remember, if a person doesn't take their weaknesses seriously these vulnerabilities will lead to great damage from the attacks of temptation. Every weakness requires a prevention plan – phone calls, meetings and establishing ongoing boundaries.

Nehemiah Principle Eleven
Accountability is always in a group, not in only one person.

You will also notice that Nehemiah uses a lot of warriors, never just one. Warriors stand together. A powerful illustration is a scene from the movie *Gladiator*. The main character, Maximus, has been made into a slave and forced to fight as a gladiator. He's in the Coliseum, where the plan of the Romans is that he and a group of other gladiators are going to be slaughtered in a re-creation of the second battle of Carthage. Maximus gathers the men around and says to them, "Whatever comes through those gates, if we stay together, we will survive." As the Roman chariots enter the arena, the gladiators stand together, lock shields, and fend off the attack. Maximus continually exhorts them, "Stay as one." Because of their connected strength, they survive against superior odds.

That movie scene is a great picture of accountability: People standing as one, together. *Whatever the world or Satan sends your way, if you stand together with others in recovery, you can survive.*

The most common mistake concerning accountability is made by well-intentioned Christians who think that they can have an accountability "partner." This plan is foolishness. Haven't you lied skillfully enough to defeat one partner, or even two? After all, we addicts are usually great liars. We know how to get by without revealing the truth, especially if we only have to convince one person. You need a group who really know you and who won't be fooled when you're having times of weakness.

There is strength in fellowship. Loneliness is one of the reasons you acted out in the first place. *Fellowship is the answer.* Make no mistake, though, about the meaning of "fellowship." I'm defining fellowship as those who really know you. It isn't your average Bible study group or church-based class. Those in your group must really know everything about you – all your secret sins, your wounds, your temptations, your feelings. It's also important for them to be encouragers, and not disciplinarians. All of us respond much better to positive reinforcement.

One of my principles is that:

Fellowship equals freedom from lust.

You must identify at least four or five others who are willing to stand with you. These people should know all your acting out behaviors, all your rituals, all of the ways you've fantasized, and all of your emotional history. Checking in with them won't take long because they know you so well already. They'll quickly be able to give you feedback about what you should do to protect yourself in the days to come. These safe people will stand with you in the gap against all attacks.

Nehemiah Principle Twelve
Our motivation for transformation should be selfless.

There is a great battle cry in the fourteenth verse of chapter four. Nehemiah says, *"Don't be afraid of them [the attackers]. Remember the Lord, who is great and awesome, and fight for your brothers, your sons and your daughters, your wives and your homes"* (NIV). The great reminder here, again, is that the battle belongs to the Lord. But there's much more in this exhortation: The battle is also to be fought for others.

After the great catastrophe of September 11, 2001, we were all inspired by the example of the firefighters and police officers who sacrificed their lives in attempts to save others. That is what heroes do. That is what warriors do. You should be no different. Your motivation should be to prevent injuring anybody else around you. It should be to never again see the look of pain on the face of someone close to you, like your wife. It should be to keep your home safe for your children and others. And it should be to provide leadership and an example for your brothers who also seek to be transformed.

If your motivation is to avoid all personal consequences and if your recovery is fear based you'll probably fail. Fear only lasts so long. When it subsides, you'll be tempted to act out again. Motivation that's proactive and includes eventually helping others is usually much more successful. After you're stable in your recovery, focus your energy outward. Get out of your selfishness. Be willing to lead a life of sacrifice.

I've had the opportunity to speak to several military groups. When we think about battles and fighting wars, what do we honor in soldiers? It's that they are willing to die for their country. This willingness to sacrifice, even to the point of death, is part of what it means to be transformed. Would you be willing to die for someone beyond yourself? What about your children? Your wife? Your sisters and brothers? When you can answer "yes" to those questions, you'll be successful in your journey of transformation.

Nehemiah Principle Thirteen
Accountability means building as well as defending

Here is one last point from chapter four. Notice in verses 16 and 17 that half of the men built and half stood guard with their spears, bows, and shields. Even the men who carried material carried the supplies in one hand and a sword in the other. The picture is that there was a balance between building and defending a balance in equal measure. Those who only have a defensive strategy in place get really tired of always being on guard. It takes a lot of energy to defend all the time. Defending is only negative. It's about the things you don't do.

The challenge of this picture in Nehemiah chapter four is that we must be *building* something, not just defending. AA says; if you're going to stop something start something. We're all built to be creative and productive. We long to build. God put creative energy into our brains so that we will "be fruitful and increase in number," Gen. 1:28. Use the energy and effort that you put into acting out and put it into building and envision what you are going to build. The real journey of transformation is about going forward in positive directions. Our healing must be proactive. It's not enough to be removing the rubble from your life, or even to be guarding against slips and relapse. Genuine and lasting transformation requires building an entire way of living life that goes far beyond your acting out behavior.

Nehemiah Principle Fourteen
Accountability means putting positive things into your life.

The program of recovery can't be about deprivation, or it will fail. Many falter in their recovery because all of their program activity is negative. Remember that you're probably an abandonment victim. A voice inside you screams for love, attention, and activity. If all you do is continue to deny these basic needs, that same voice will continue to scream – and will probably get louder. You'll remain vulnerable to the false substitutes you've historically used to meet your legitimate needs and medicate your feelings.

Positive actions are discussed in Principle Seven where we talk about asking the Lord to give you a vision. Remember some of those practical, positive steps. Examples include:

- Eating better
- Getting more rest
- Getting a medical check-up
- Exercising
- Inviting a friend for coffee
- Making a date with your spouse
- Making an appointment with a therapist or counselor
- Going to a workshop
- Getting into a Bible study
- Buying yourself some music that inspires you
- Doing anything just for fun

This isn't a complete list, but it provides some sample ideas. You'll notice that most of these items concern self-care, which is something most addicts have difficulty doing. Many of us got the false message that taking care of ourselves is "selfish." The reality is that historically you *have been* selfish, but not in this sense. You've been selfishly providing yourself with false substitutes for comfort, excitement, fun and pleasure. Part of building a healthy life is to find positive ways of meeting your needs.

Every project begins with an idea, and every idea leads to a picture of what will be built. Every artist, every builder, and every writer has always begun with the picture of the finished project in their mind. When you finish this principle I want you to have a beginning vision of what you are going to build. Here are some areas where you might consider building, physical, character, spiritual and relational. In the L.I.F.E. Recovery Group Meeting Guidelines we suggest that participants share with the group the positive steps they have been taken that week. This practice is a great encouragement and gives an opportunity for accountability during check-in.as well.

Nehemiah Principle Fifteen
Accountability is an on-going, lifelong process,
but God provides sustaining energy.

Our original adrenaline that gave us so much energy for the start of the project eventually wears off. Now we come to the mundane tasks and the work can be expensive. This is when our heart and motivations are tested. Chapter five of Nehemiah reports that the work gets tiring and expensive. The strength of the workers gives out. The rebuilding costs mount, and some begin extracting taxes and expenses. However, instead of simply helping the cause, these workers are making a profit. Some of the people even go so far as to sell their own children into slavery, which was a custom of the time.

In my own first year of recovery, I went to therapy and support groups all the time. I was scared enough to go to something recovery oriented almost every day. The effort was expensive and it was tiring. I remember thinking during that time, "When does this end? When do I get to stop being an addict?" Pat Carnes discovered in some of his early research that the period between the sixth and the twelfth months of healing is the most dangerous time for relapse. I think the main reason is because early recovery is so exhausting. Another reason is because we're still facing the consequences of our addiction during the first year, and life hasn't necessarily become much better. During this time, we might be tempted to go back into slavery, back to our behaviors just to cope with our exhaustion. The vicious cycle begins again.

It's important you accept that doing the work of healing will be expensive and exhausting. Rebuilding is difficult, but God is sufficient. Don't sell yourself back into slavery.
Read chapter 5 verse 13. Nehemiah reports, *"I also shook out the folds of my robe and said, 'In this way may God shake out of His house and possessions every man who does not keep this promise. So may such a man be shaken out and emptied!' At this the whole assembly said, 'Amen,' and praised the LORD. And the people did as they had promised."*
As someone in the process of transformation, keep your promises!

This principle from Nehemiah is a reminder that when you think you can't go on - or you think you've finished your recovery work or that you're healed – realize you're not. Keep reaching out for help and support. Look further to a successful recovery model, the practices found in the *LRM L.I.F.E. Recovery Model* http://www.freedomeveryday.org/lrm to help you re-evaluate your recovery plan or take begin giving back, sharing your story and serving those still caught in the trap of addiction.

On the day I am writing this I had breakfast with a longtime friend of mine who has been sober now for 20 years. He told me about a new meeting that he had just started and that he was going back to all the basics of doing all the work all over again. This is a healthy way of life, and he doesn't plan to change a thing. I know that maintaining fellowship and accountability are crucial to my own journey. Be sure to watch against falling into the dangerous trap of thinking you've "made it," are "healed," or can now "let down your guard." When it comes to change and healing, do whatever it takes, however much it costs, and God will find a way. The biblical wisdom portrayed here is that when a person isn't greedy or selfish, God does provide, a theme reiterated in many other parts of the Bible.

Nehemiah Principle Sixteen
When tempted, remain committed to transformation without wavering.

In Nehemiah chapter six, the wall is nearing completion. The enemies are frustrated with the results of their frontal assaults, so they come up with three different schemes to defeat the rebuilding project. True to the "cunning" nature of addiction (and Satan), these attacks are much more subtle.

First, the enemies invite Nehemiah to a meeting outside of the city to talk about their differences. But instead of this reasonable-sounding plan, they actually are plotting to kill. This scheme is the plot of 'distraction." The enemies are being polite and civil, and it might seem rational to have a meeting. It's tempting to ignore the potential consequences of getting involved with the enemy, especially if you believe you have a "good" reason. Rest assured that the enemies of transformation have a hidden (and evil) agenda. Understand that Satan will come after you with very subtle, civil, and rational sounding distractions. It may simply be something like, "You've been working so hard, why not take a break? Have a little fun." Or perhaps Satan deceives you through your own self-talk: "I'm tired. Why do I have to spend so much energy working my program? I have such restrictive boundaries maybe I can relax them a little." You may be tempted to stop thinking of yourself as an "addict" and decide you've gotten beyond your earlier temptations.
Maybe it's okay to (_____ *fill in the blank*) without accountability if you're only going to (_____ *fill in the blank*). Or surely by now you can handle (_____ *fill in the blank*) after all, you have a legitimate reason to (_____ *fill in the blank*). Do you see how easy it can be to justify behavior?

I remember when I came out of treatment and my brother knew I had changed, he said to me, "Mark, when can we be a normal family again?" The answer to that is, "Hopefully, never." In other words, "I'm not coming down from the wall."

Temptation comes in many disguises and many voices, including your own. Remember, you're dealing with spiritual warfare. Hear the battle cry of Nehemiah: "I am carrying on a great project and cannot come down." It's not a complicated decision he ponders over. Your work is important. Don't let the enemy distract you. Nehemiah is a man of persistence, fortitude and simplicity. Take his example to heart. Don't lose sight of the great work you're doing, and never waiver from your commitment to transformation.

Nehemiah Principle Seventeen
Transformation targets you for rumors and personal attacks.

The enemies step up the attack as chapter six unfolds. In the second scheme, they circulate a rumor that Nehemiah is trying to usurp the power of the king. The enemies are basically accusing him of grandiosity. They claim Nehemiah is trying to be too powerful and is too full of himself. They suggest he come to the meeting (outside the city, remember) and discuss his intentions.

Be aware that your journey of transformation will target you for rumors. Some of the attacking voices will come from the religious folk. People may accuse you of trying to be something that you're not, or condemn you for being "selfish" in making healthy choices. They may question your participation in a support group program. Other attacking voices will be secular ones. They'll taunt you for being "self-righteous" about your morals. Don't be surprised if you're accused of being "judgmental" for maintaining standards for healthy intimacy. People from both religious and secular communities will wonder about your recovery program in general and believe you're trying to escape responsibility by hiding behind an "addiction."

In an article in *Playboy* magazine, I was accused (along with others) of inventing the concept of sexual addiction so that "professionals" could make money treating it. The assumption was that sexual addiction doesn't exist. In another instance a former colleague of mine who was jealous of my success accused me of having an affair with another colleague. All of it was not true but for some who heard it, like those at a large national ministry, the damage is still something I'm trying to overcome. You don't know how many times the words of Nehemiah come to me: "You are just making it up out of your head." These rumors and attacks can get really tiring and sometimes frightening. You will often be misunderstood about your feelings and motivations as you seek to be transformed into a closer image of Christ.

These false accusations against Nehemiah are the same kind of rumors that Jewish leaders circulated about Jesus. They said He was trying to be King. They dragged Him in front of Pilate and accused Him of being a radical and a revolutionary. Pilate knew these charges were crazy and thought he could resolve the problem when he stood Jesus next to Barabbas and asked the people their choice of whom he should release. Barabbas was a known revolutionary, and Pilate must have thought this solution was a way to "wash his hands" of the matter and get the people to do his work for him. Of course, Pilate's plan backfired to Jesus' ultimate glory and our eternal salvation.

The point is that you'll deal with misunderstanding and perhaps false rumors. It's easy to get distracted by trying to explain yourself. I, at least, tend to get defensive, which only robs me of energy I need to focus on my work of transformation. Nehemiah provides a better example of how to deal with this kind of attack. He says to his accusers, "Nothing like what you're saying is happening; you are just making it up out of your head" (verse 8). Nehemiah responds simply and directly, and then he quickly gets back to work.

He is, though, in touch with his emotions regarding this attack. He recognizes the enemies are trying to frighten him and the others. The attackers hope, "Their hands will get too weak for the work, and it will not be completed" (verse 9). Nehemiah prays that God will "strengthen my hands" as he leads the people. At times you'll need to pray for strength and ask supportive friends to encourage you in the ongoing work.

You do not have to be fully understood to pursue your "great work" of transformation. You may be falsely accused of pride, arrogance, ambition, or selfishness. You may be stung by rumors. You'll certainly feel distracted and discouraged. You'll fear your hands are too weak for their work. Consider Nehemiah's response and renew your courage and commitment.

Nehemiah Principle Eighteen
Transformation results in a willingness to sacrifice even your own life.

The truth of the situation is that the work is very dangerous. There is one final plot. An invalid by the name of Shemaiah invites Nehemiah to come with him to the temple where they will be safe. The work is dangerous he says, and if Nehemiah is going to continue his good effort of rebuilding the wall, he must stay safe. Nehemiah's response is powerful: "Should a man like me run away or try to save his own life?"

As you seek to build and lead a transformed life, at times you'll be tempted to retreat to safety. Others may even encourage you to take the easy path of self-protection. For example, when you're being successful in living a pure life and are finding opportunities to share the message about God's transforming power, you may be tempted (or advised) not to share your story because it might harm your reputation. I had many people try to convince me to stop traveling after the terrorist attack on September 11, 2002. In a variety of ways you may be pressured to stop your important work.

Nehemiah, though, wisely discerned that Shemaiah was no true friend out to protect his best interest. He knew that Shemaiah actually was in on a plot to kill him inside the supposed safety of the temple itself. My guess is that Nehemiah's response would have been the same even if he wasn't aware of Shemaiah's true intentions. Nehemiah would have refused to retreat from his mission.

For those of us who seek to change and heal, often the work will seem very dangerous too. It will feel at times that we must take a certain amount of risk to do the new behaviors we have been told will heal us. For one thing, when we learn how to start telling the truth to others, we will confront the anxiety that gets us to think "if they really knew me, they would hate me or leave me." Maybe for you it will mean having the courage to go to L.I.F.E. Recovery Group or confessing your sins to spiritual authority. I have often been amazed at how courageous those in recovery have been who resign and find another job, perhaps for less money, because it provides them with more time at home and more safety.

Our response must be the same. In Ephesians 5:1-2, Paul says we should be "imitators" of God and be willing, like Christ, to give ourselves up as a "fragrant offering and sacrifice to God." Sacrifice can mean taking risks to do the right thing, even if it makes us feel afraid. Obviously, we won't be perfect at courageously continuing in our work, no matter the risk. Only Jesus was perfectly self-sacrificing. But we can draw strength from His example, face our fears, and ignore the voices that suggest we abandon our work.

Accountability will mean our accountability partners will often need to remind us that the enemy sends false messages and plots and schemes to get us away from the work. Accountability reminds you to stay on the wall! There is a constant theme in both Nehemiah 5 and 6. Nehemiah is willing to do whatever it takes as long as it takes. Undoubtedly he is tired and frightened, but at every temptation, every problem that arises, and every distraction to stay focused on the task, he stays on the wall.

Although the wall is finished, the work inside the city is just beginning. Recovery is building healthy boundaries so that the enemy will have a much harder time attacking us. These Principles establish those boundaries. Those boundaries are the beginning. Now you face the lifelong interior work you must do. That will affect your family and all your relationships. You will rebuild your house, and your legacy will be great.

Tying It All Together

I have gone to such length to teach these 18 principles from Nehemiah because I believe they provide a wonderful example of the total process of living in freedom everyday. This story of humility, courage, action, focus, and dependence on God illustrates the Seven Principles outlined in this L.I.F.E. Recovery Guide. Rebuilding the wall is a picture of transforming your life.

This process involves surrender on a daily basis. Regardless of the challenges, whether from within your own heart or from external sources, being transformed means surrendering your life, your will, and the outcomes to God.

Taking life one day at a time and maintaining accountability will be the core of your program for the rest of your life. This reality isn't just because you're an addict. It's because you are someone who seeks to follow Christ.

Time is God's

Before we finish with Nehemiah, notice a statement at the end of chapter six. How long do you think the building project takes? A dozen years? Maybe only eight to ten years? Surely such a huge project takes three or four years, at least, right?

Wrong. Verse 15 reports, *"So the wall was completed on the 25th of Elul, in 52 days. When all our enemies heard about this, all the surrounding nations were afraid and lost their self-*

confidence, because they realized that this work had been done with the help of our God." Did you catch that? *The wall was finished in only 52 days*!

In one sense, the process of transformation is a lifelong endeavor. We're never "finished" with the journey of becoming transformed into a sacrificial life in Christ. We continually must be about the task of rebuilding the walls – of our hearts, our lives, our families, and our relationship with Christ.

But in another sense, the intensity of the work will not last as long as you may fear. It won't always be as hard as it is in the beginning. The struggle to maintain sobriety will ease. Integrity will take the place of dishonesty. The pain of the past will recede. Relationships will be restored. Wounds will heal. Fellowship and community will replace loneliness. You'll discover you've even been surprised by joy – that your spirit knows a peace that passes understanding.

Another great slogan from Alcoholics Anonymous is found in the "Promises of Recovery." After listing a variety of positives, the recovering person will experience, the *"Big Book,"* which gives a timeframe for when these promises will be fulfilled: "before you're half way through" of the first intense part of your journey, perhaps after only 52 days.

During those times when you're tired and lonely and frightened, remember Nehemiah's story and be encouraged by his example. You, too, are doing a great work as you build a life of purity, and good things may start coming to you in a shorter time than you might imagine.

Time belongs to God, and He will guide your journey from beginning to end.

Definitions

Communication is essential to intimate fellowship. Fellowship is vital to L.I.F.E. - Living In Freedom Everyday. Group discussions, feedback, and presentations are the life-blood of support and encouragement. Effective communication and fellowship require that we understand each other – that we speak the same language. Standard terminology is a tool for clear communication, and agreement about definitions allows each L.I.F.E. Recovery Group member to communicate easily with others in his own group and in the ministry network across the country. Each group member should study the following definitions to eliminate as much confusion as possible in regard to terminology. (These definitions may also provide a productive discussion topic for a L.I.F.E. Recovery Group meeting.) The definitions are based on my understanding gleaned from talking to hundreds of recovering people from a variety of geographic locations. Every group, though, may have local or personal understandings that are important in their setting. What's crucial is that the group discusses variations in meanings so that everyone can be clear about them.

90 Days

The term "Ninety Days" comes from the AA slogan "90 days, 90 meetings," which refers to the first three months of an alcoholic's recovery. Many times it's necessary for a person to go to a meeting every day for the first 90 days in order to remain sober. This commitment is a good one for all addicts, as well. In the beginning of your healing journey or after a relapse, committing to a "90 in 90" is an excellent plan.

Ninety days has also been applied to the period of time a sex addict may choose to be sexually abstinent with self and others, including his spouse. (You'll find more information about the concept of a ninety days' abstinence period in Principle Four, Assignment One.)

Abstinence

Abstinence is the act or practice of refraining from indulging an appetite or desire, especially for alcoholic drink or sexual intercourse; the state of restraint being without a substance, drug, as alcohol, heroin or behavior on which one is dependent.

Accountability Partner

This is any person who agrees to be in your network of people holding you accountable. A common mistake is thinking that you can have one accountability partner. I've never known a person to recover when he's only accountable to one person. One of your accountability partners can be your *sponsor*, but your spouse shouldn't be either your sponsor or an accountability partner. The word "partner" usually describes more mutuality in the relationship than is typical with a sponsor.

Acting Out/Acting In

Acting out refers to the practice of engaging in sinful, dysfunctional, coping, escaping or medicating behaviors. "Acting in" refers to rigidly controlling behaviors in an unhealthy way. It often means that a behavior is being strictly avoided, but the person isn't growing emotionally and spiritually. "Acting in" is often used synonymously to describe those anorexic with food or those who are sexually anorexic. "Acting In" also can be seen as an act of denial of appropriate self-care and nurturing, acts of deprivation that harm the care and value of self. "Acting out" and "acting in" are really opposite ends of the same continuum. They both can be attempts to control painful memories or emotions.

Addiction

Christopher J. Charleton, M.A., LCSW, is a specialist in the resolution of addictive and cross-addictive behaviors. Charleton is a member of The Society for the Advancement of Sexual Health (SASH), The International Association of Eating Disorder Professionals (IAEDP), and the National Association of Christians in Recovery, and the author of the book Relapse.

Charleton states, ultimately, addiction means to **declare** that I am *"bound, devoted, or delivered over to someone or something."* (Online Etymological Dictionary, © Douglas Harper) Addictive behaviors, attitudes, and frames of reference which distort and fragment God's original design for us violate our sense of self. We betray ourselves by abandoning relationship with God and others for relationship with addictive substances and processes which culminate in isolation and estrangement. Addiction stems from painful ruptures and resultant betrayals associated with crucial life relationships.

Historically, the word "addiction" has been controversial in the Christian community. Some fear the concept of addiction removes personal responsibility for sinful behavior. Some believe those who call themselves addicts blame their personal decisions on an "addiction." All truly repentant and humble addicts, however, always accept personal responsibility for their actions.

The medical and psychological community has several universal criteria for determining if a substance or a behavior is an addiction:

1. **Use of the substance or behavior has become "unmanageable."** This means the addict has tried to stop, over and over again, but can't. There is a history of failed attempts. Some clinicians believe there must be a two-year history, at least, of an unmanageable pattern for a person to be labeled an addict. The word "powerless" has also been used to describe this pattern. Sometimes addicts refer to themselves as "out of control." Even when an addict creates destructive consequences for himself by sinful behavior, it's not enough to get him to stop.

2. **The addiction gets worse over time.** This means that more and more of the substance or behavior will be needed over time to achieve the same effect. An alcoholic knows, for example, that as he continues to drink, he'll need more and more alcohol to get "high" or drunk. Sex addicts know that they need more and more sexual activity to achieve the same "high" of the acting out experience. This escalation can take two forms. The most basic is that the addict does more and more of the same kind of behavior. I've known, for example, people who start masturbating once a month and progress to once a day or more in the course of their addiction. For some addicts progression means they'll need new kinds of acting out experiences to achieve the same "high". It's important to remember that most addicts won't progress to illegal, highly dangerous, or sexually offending kinds of behavior. Some do, but the majority do not. Addicts may be able to stop their behaviors for periods of time, but until they find healing and the core issues driving their addiction, they will always return to them. Over time, a pattern of repeated failure will be evident.

3. **Tolerance is one reason for the factor of progression.** Medical science is discovering new things about the human brain that broaden our understanding of addictive behavior. The chemistry of the brain adjusts to whatever an addict puts into it. Over time the brain demands more to achieve the same effect. For alcoholics and drug addicts, the brain adjusts to substance and requires more. Thinking about sex and engaging in sexual behavior requires that the brain produce the brain chemistry to achieve sexual response. New research is finding that the sexual chemistry of the brain can also become tolerant, which means more and more thought or activity is necessary to have the same brain chemistry effects — the feelings of arousal, excitement, and pleasure. In many ways, sex addicts are drug addicts, as well as any behavior that elevates or lowers the neurochemistry in the brain. Workaholics become dependent on the adrenaline rush of expectations and deadlines, as a result we become high on the drugs produced in our own brain.

4. **Because of the brain chemistry involved, addicts use the thoughts and behaviors that produce the neurochemical highs to either raise or lower their mood**. We say then that addicts "medicate" their feelings. If an addict is depressed, lonely or bored, they can think of exciting encounters, either remembered or imagined, and the arousal part of the response produces chemicals that raise his mood. If an addict is stressed, anxious or fearful, they will tend to think of the relationship or a romance quality of the encounter. These associated brain chemicals create a feeling of well-being and contentment that lowers their mood. Most addicts are capable of both kinds of thoughts, and, therefore, can both raise and lower their moods depending on their feelings at the moment.

5. **Finally, addicts act out despite negative consequences.** Addicts don't pay attention to negative consequences and are in what's commonly called "denial." They also usually "minimize" or "rationalize" their acting out, despite the consequences. Until an addict decides to surrender control of their fears that prevent getting help, they'll continue to act out. Addicts may also continue to act out because it's usually a slow and insidious form

of suicide, instead of immediately deadly. They know at some level they're destroying their lives, but their depression prevents them from caring.

Addictive Condition

Alcohol is merely a substance. Same with marijuana, cocaine and food. Gambling is merely an activity. Same with work, exercise and sex. The point is, these things do not *create* addicts. They are simply the activities and substances that addicts *use*. So when we speak of addiction, we must understand that our concern is not with these activities and substances but with something else, something that exists independent of these things. We can remove every substance and activity from the life of an addict, but nevertheless, he is still an addict.

In fact, sobriety is simply a voluntary abstinence from all activities and substances in the life of an addict that are used to perpetuate his addiction. Stop using, stop doing, and you are sober. This is a good start, but you have yet to be made well because, as we stated above, something else independent of the addictive behaviors remains. This something else is what we call the addictive condition.

The addictive condition consists of a whole host of issues. Neurochemical imbalances. Abuse. Abandonment. Arrested development. Fragmentation. An incapacity for emotional wholeness and intimacy both relational and spiritual. These are the things that create addicts. These issues predate our addictive behaviors, they exist independent of our addictive behaviors, and they serve to perpetuate our addictive behaviors. We can achieve sobriety from our addictive *behaviors*, but if we fail to address our addictive *condition* we cannot heal. *Christopher J. Charleton*

Bottom Line

A "bottom line" is a boundary that refers to the distinction between which behaviors are tolerable and which ones aren't. An addict may have a bottom line as to what behaviors are outside of their sobriety definition, such as not spending time with others who still engage in a particular behavior. A spouse may also have a definition about which behaviors would cause them to leave if they happened again. This kind of bottom line is sometimes referred to as a "line in the sand."

"Bottom line" behaviors are those that if engaged in may jeopardize our recovery plan and ability to grow toward healthy intimate relationships. If someone is recovering from romance obsession one of their "bottom lines" may include not listening to romantic music or watching romantic movies because entertaining those thoughts or activities would set them up for failure. Perhaps a shopaholic would no longer carry credit or debit cards or spend time at a shopping mall. Similarly a workaholic's "bottom line" may require strict adherence to leaving the job after 8 hours even if work is left undone. Re-evaluate and update bottom lines frequently. Our success with bottom lines give us hope that we will, in time, reach our top lines. For more information on this process, see Top Line.

Boundaries

In simplest terms, boundaries are guidelines for safety. They define which behaviors should and shouldn't occur in relationships and in families. They **pro**scribe what behaviors should *not* be allowed, and when these boundaries are violated, that is "invasion." Boundaries also **pre**scribe what behaviors *should* happen. When these boundaries are violated (or not upheld, to describe it another way), then "abandonment" happens. Some people have non-existent or "loose" boundaries, which frequently causes them to be harmed in some way. Other people have too high or "rigid" boundaries. They won't allow themselves to be loved or nurtured. Many people don't know how to establish their own boundaries. They might be codependent. Other people don't know how to observe boundaries. They might be perpetrators of harm or abuse. Stating your boundaries is a way of asking for safety, which is a different practice from making "demands." A demand is a request for more immediate action, which may have more to do with fear and anger than it does with personal safety

Boundaries are limits for our protection as well as for another. There are six domains listed below to identify types of boundaries. Physical and emotional boundaries are generally known and understood; however, we'll take a look at other boundary domains that may not be so well known.

1. **Physical boundaries** are defined as what I will allow others to <u>do to me</u> physically, i.e. touch, physical proximity, etc., usually a distance just outside the reach of the others with whom you interact; as well as what I will <u>do to others</u>, also relating to touch or proximity. Who will I allow inside this perimeter; under what circumstances, etc.? No one is entitled to "invade my space," nor do I allow myself to invade the space of others.

2. **Emotional boundary** is defined as my freedom to own and express my emotional response to others or events. Emotional expression is the result of how I perceive and interprets events. Emotions can act as an alarm system or an expression that the environment is safe, comfortable, joyous, etc. Emotions are semi-automatic in that they may occur without conscious thought, or I may consciously decide how I will respond. My emotional boundary allows me to own and openly express, or repress or tolerate others. I own my emotions, and I allow you to own your expressions. In this way, neither is emotionally abused by the other. No one is entitled to tell me what I ought, or ought not, to feel.

3. **Intellectual boundaries** define my right to possess and define what I know. My thinking is my thinking; erroneous, flawed as it may be, it is mine. Understanding a proper intellectual boundary is to recognize that I know and what I know, and that is OK. The best way to describe this definition is by an example: as a child/adolescent growing up I was continually told that I was stupid and would never amount to anything, was too dumb to learn anything. That is an example of the invasion of my intellectual boundary. Statements in this example, for some, are damaging to their intellectual development. To establish and maintain a healthy intellectual boundary is to protect what you know without invading the intellectual boundary of others. No one knows everything, but all know something.

4. **Spiritual boundaries** relate to a healthy sense of self. We relate to this domain as self-esteem. Spiritual boundaries, also, while not religion, involve religion in its expression. Remember, Jesus allowed the rich young ruler, to whom He offered the saving grace that he was seeking, to have his liberty to walk away (Luke18:18-23). While Jesus was saddened by his response, He did not pursue him. In many ways, the previous boundaries have helped to define this boundary – to define who I am and who you are.

5. **Sexual boundaries** are the limits that we place on our thinking and acting out with regard to our sexuality. They also include the physical aspects regarding the manner in which we will allow others to behave toward us and the ways in which we will behave sexually toward others. This subject is addressed more fully in another L.I.F.E. Recovery Guide in this series.

6. **Social boundaries** govern our social interactions that demonstrate concern for others and engage in behaviors that build relationships with others. - Spiller

Codependency

"Codependency is the fallacy of trying to control interior feelings by controlling people, things, and events on the outside." *Love is a Choice,* Drs. Hemfelt, Minirth and Meier.

"Codependency is an interactive style of behavior attempting to minimize the risk of abandonment and rejection. Its origin lies in the survival strategies of a child desperate to win the love, affection, and attention of its parents. When parents are overwhelmed with their own life-dominating pain (disabled or preoccupied with financial, health or other concerns), the child unwittingly becomes conditioned to not further "burden" the parent. To do so would risk the parent's wrath, leading to physical punishment or being shunned. Correspondingly, the child develops a survival strategy utilizing hypervigilance to safeguard against rejection. Consequently, the child begins to consciously or unconsciously suppress itself, denying its own needs and wants for the purpose of being loved and accepted. The problem, however, is that the child is not actively being loved by the parent. In order to facilitate a bond with the parent, the child operates under the delusion that being perfect or self-sufficient will guarantee the love and attachment it so desperately longs for. This formula utilized to procure love is driven by self-abandonment - the child has to give by not being "needy" in order to get. As the child employs this survival strategy in later life, it engages in relationships where there is no reciprocity. They become the wellspring of infinite giving which "sustains" the relationship. To let one's true needs or wants be known would risk relational destruction. Underlying such codependent gestures of love is a chronic sense of terror, emptiness, loneliness and resentment. Codependency masquerading as love can never accomplish Christ's purpose because it is driven by fear; more specifically, by the fear of abandonment. 1 John 4:18 says *"Perfect love casts out all fear, in fear is great torment, and in fear love cannot be made perfect."* Although codependent-based relationships appear to be the ultimate in Christ-like servanthood and marital bliss, in truth they are characterized by underlying misery, bitterness, resentment, and fear. If marriage and friendships necessitate gaining the love, approval and acceptance through the abandonment of oneself, then the relationship can only work to the degree that the codependent does not exist." *Christopher J. Charleton, Relapse - 2012.*

Codependency was first used in the Alcoholics Anonymous (AA) community to refer to anyone who was in relationship with an alcoholic. The assumption was that these individuals tolerated drinking, as evidenced by their remaining in the relationship. These individuals, then, were considered "dependent" on the alcoholic. And since the alcoholic is dependent on alcohol, these people are "codependent" on alcohol. These people (usually spouses) tolerate an alcoholic and his/her drinking behavior out of their fear of being alone. It's more important for the codependent to maintain the relationship than it is to confront drinking and the problems it creates. As understanding about addiction has broadened beyond alcoholism to sexual and other forms of compulsive behaviors, the term codependent has come to refer to anyone who tolerates problematic or addictive behavior.

From this basic definition, many have written about codependency and said that codependents abandon their own needs and attend to the needs of the addict. They are more interested in maintaining the approval and presence of the addict than they are in speaking the truth. This objective causes them to ignore their own needs and wants and sacrifice themselves. This sacrifice is out of their fears, not out of their strengths.

Codependents often "enable" the addict by making excuses for him or her and generally looking the other way. They also perform many of the tasks that an addict should be responsible for, which led many to term codependents "doers." Accordingly, all that codependents "do" may save addicts from consequences, which often earn codependents the title of "rescuers." Finally, since codependents *seem* selfless, some have called them (and they may see themselves as) "martyrs." Essentially, codependency is a fear and anxiety-based disorder in which the individual has an addiction to approval.

Please be aware that any labels, such as codependency or co-addiction, are used only for the purpose of identifying problems that need to be healed. We should always seek to use these terms in love and not in judgment. Some primary partners (spouses) soundly reject these labels as humiliating. They might say, "It's his or her problem, not mine." These spouses could benefit from exploring why they choose to stay in the relationship.

Co-Addiction

Co-addicts are people who are in a *primary* relationship (such as marriage) with an addict. "Co-addict" defines a relationship between two people, just as "aunt" and "niece" indicates a certain relationship. Co-addicts may or may not suffer from the symptoms of codependency. Some co-addicts may not be consciously aware of their partner's addiction. They may seem strong and self-assured, but this appearance, too, can be a disguise for insecurity.

Compartmentalizing

In James 4:8, the brother of Christ says that we can be "double-minded." This term means that various parts of our brain can be at war with each other, which is certainly true with addiction. Paul, in Romans 7, says that we don't always do what we want to do, and that we often do what we *don't* want to do. One reason for this failure can be due to our "compartmentalizing." We segregate off parts of ourselves and aren't "unified." Another word for this state is "dissociating," which is a clinical term for a defense mechanism that refers to trying not to think about (or even to be aware of) something that is painful. Addicts often compartmentalize their sinful behavior and then deny that it even exists in reality.

Core Wounds – Traumatology

Addictive behavior is widely understood to be an attempt to medicate the pain of some past trauma or relational wounding that has not been resolved. The original emotional damage thus becomes a core issue, and the fact that it remains unresolved becomes the often subconscious excuse for the relationally and spiritually destructive behavior. The behavioral controls we impose, emotionally and spiritually, on childhood traumas as we mature into adulthood often serve only to rationalize and entrench the addictive behavior. We numb the pain over and over, often with increasing levels of the pain-killing behavior just to maintain that numbness. Satan is always there to use and intensify that inability to identify and express emotions, and to further disable our ability to have relationship with those we care about or even with God Himself. This L.I.F.E. Recovery Guide can help you invite Christ into the painful emotions associated with your suffering, and identify those core wounds from the past. Jesus himself expressed emotions in very open and often strong ways: He was moved to tears in the Garden, and to righteous anger in clearing the money changers from the Temple. Many of us have not been taught how to process and express such feelings. In order to heal, we must be able to express emotions in a manner that is consistent and constructive, and to deal with those core wounds in a safe environment such as a L.I.F.E. Recovery support group, where real relationships are built—open, transparent and accountable.

Cross Talk

This reference simply means talking back and forth during meetings, the process of feedback. Some groups have struggled with this concept because certain members may talk too long, give too much advice, be too angry or judgmental, or simply be rude. People are encouraged at meetings to be good listeners and not to be amateur counselors. Members should always seek to be loving in their feedback. Members in L.I.F.E. Recovery Groups learn to express their feelings and process pain and as these skills are practiced confidence builds and they are applied in daily life outside group. L.I.F.E. Recovery Groups not only allow cross talk, but encourage this dialog. A safe group provides the best environment to learn healthy intimacy skills and is essential for effective recovery. See the Safety Guidelines in the Meeting Guide section.

Cruising

This term refers to any ritual behavior (described in Principle One, Assignment Two) designed to find a partner to act out with sexually or relationally. Cruising rituals may include dress, appearance, facial expressions, flirting, "hanging out" in certain places, or any variety of behaviors designed to find or attract a partner.

Cycle

A cycle is a predictable pattern where one thought or behavior leads to others that eventually lead back to the original thought or emotion. The addiction cycle is explained in Principle One, Assignment Two, and the recovery cycle is described in Principle Six, Assignment Two.

Denial

Simply put, denial is avoiding or "denying" reality. Fear of consequences, such as others' reactions or our own painful emotions, is the usual cause for avoiding the truth. Denial involves both direct lies and the avoidance of reality.

Entitlement

All addicts need to "excuse" their behaviors. They search for reasons why it's okay to act out. One of the main excuses is called "entitlement," which means that the addicts "deserve" to act out. Some addicts keep a balance sheet in their heads and feel that when they've done enough good behaviors, they're entitled to do some bad behaviors. Some addicts feel so unjustly treated in life (martyrs) that they believe it's only fair for them to get something for themselves. Anger and narcissism are usually behind the feeling of entitlement.

Family of Origin

Your family of origin generally refers to your immediate biological family: your parents and brothers and sisters. It can also mean any people who have lived with you under the same roof. Examples might include stepparents, uncles, aunts, grandparents and cousins, but "family of origin" can also indicate others who lived with you, even if they weren't biologically related to you.

Family Systems

Dr. Murray Bowen authored the Family Systems Theory. A core assumption in this theory is that an emotional system that evolved over several billion years governs all human relationship systems. Bowen posited that "transmission between family members appeared to be based on prolonged association." Bowen further purported that "there seems to be a link to the deep inclination of human beings to imitate one another". Bowen has done extensive study in the area of family-of-origin issues. He is responsible for developing many family-of-origin perspectives and theories. Bowen believed that "individuals could not be understood apart from their family." Bowen believed that "the degree of unresolved attachment, or indifference between parent and child influenced how well a person functioned throughout their life." Dr. Murray Bowen explains the family as a system:

A family is a system in which each member had a role to play and rules to respect. Members of the system are expected to respond to each other in a certain way according to their role, which is determined by relationship agreements. Within the boundaries of the system, patterns develop as certain family member's behavior is caused by and causes other family member's behaviors in predictable ways.

The family system is also known as Family-of-origin. Family-of-origin is the source for launching children into adult life with the attitudes, behaviors, and skills that facilitate success. Some family-of-origin systems equipped children to be healthy functioning adults and some family-of-origin systems arrested this development. Early influences operate to shape future behavior. The shaping process occurs through the following four vehicles: "(1) parent-child emotional relationship, (2) parental guidelines, (3) parental approaches to child development, and (4) behavior modeling." The family system often sets up an individual to be vulnerable to compulsive behavior, addictive behavior, and life controlling issues. It can even go so far in modeling this type of behavior that an individual ends up imitating well into adult life.

Fantasy

Fantasy is an attempt at trauma resolution, an escape from reality imagining an *"it will be better when..."* scenario to provide a different outcome. Fantasies are thoughts about anything in an imaginary way, any preoccupation or obsessive thought patterns about the experience of using your 'coping mechanism' to change your mood or gain a sense of control and relief from your unpleasant emotional distress. We develop a dependency or affection for our behavior because of the relief (albeit temporary) that we feel. Fantasy has also been referred to as "preoccupation" –being preoccupied with the comforting thoughts and imagining the relief of your distress.

Chris Charleton, an internationally-recognized addiction/trauma expert and author of the book, *Relapse*, states that:

> "Fantasy is an intellectual process utilized to escape the powerlessness and helplessness associated with unrelenting emotional, relational and spiritual pain. Examining the Carnes addiction model clearly demonstrates that shame is the direct result of unresolved trauma and is compounded by the addictive process. Every addictive relapse intensifies and reinforces the already-existing shame. Shame is the emotional, relational and spiritual equivalent of AIDS, wherein a person attacks his or her own being. At varying levels, shame leads us to detest our existence, inundating us with feelings of inferiority, inadequacy, incompetence and unworthiness which are inescapable. It directly opposes God's proclamation of our lovability and worth.
>
> As shame becomes further entrenched within our being, fantasy becomes a desperate, last-ditch attempt to remedy the conviction of our unloveability, worthlessness and rejectability. Fantasy therefore, like the phoenix, arises from the burning embers of self-contempt and hatred to create a distraction from the immensity of our inescapable pain. Hence fantasies are an illusory and ultimately ineffective mechanism devised to

200

counter our convictions of unworthiness for relationship with God, others and ourselves. Healing from the addictive process necessitates identifying our fantasies to illuminate and ultimately conquer the shame-based convictions that are robbing us of the victory that God desires for our lives."

First Year of Recovery

There are **non-negotiable** aspects for a successful "First Year of Recovery" that are detailed in the LRM (L.I.F.E. Recovery Model). Before a successful first year of recovery can be experienced one must intentionally develop disciplines that pursue wholeness. One of these disciplines is a commitment to maintaining a recovery plan. Intentionally following this plan works toward consistent application of multiple disciplines that result in healthy intimate relationships where we are safe to express feelings and to process pain. Frequent evaluations of a recovery plan in the first year are crucial for long term success, especially at times when fulfillment appears illusive. The First Year of Recovery and the LRM can be viewed in their entirety on our website http://www.freedomeveryday.org/lrm.

Fragmentation

"Fragmentation is frequently the result of trauma. When a person experiences extreme emotional wounding from any source, a portion of his or her identity is compartmentalized in an attempt to handle or repress the resultant pain. When such trauma is repeated, the fragmentation intensifies until one makes the determination: "It is no longer safe to be who I am." Consequently much of the original personality is lost, destroyed or buried in an attempt to avoid the pain. The precious, God-ordained, original "self" with its corresponding hopes, dreams, goals and authentic desires is no longer accessible to the conscious mind. In this fragmented state, part of a person begins to operate like a wounded child who is at war with the part that functions like a rational adult. This often causes one's behavior to become erratic and disjointed, leading to relational dysfunction and intra- as well as inter-personal problems.

God's design for us is exactly the opposite of this fragmentation process. His nature, manifest in the Trinity, is the perfect example of integration: Father, Son and Holy Spirit in one unified whole. Wounding and the associated fragmentation render us incapable of recognizing God's intention for integration, and even blind us to our own disintegration. Without this integration, relational intimacy with God, ourselves and others is impossible. Fragmentation ultimately develops strongholds of resistance to God's plan for intimacy and integration. Therefore the path to ultimate healing involves breaking down those strongholds through honest self-examination and the willingness to face and grieve the pain which resulted from the trauma which shattered the original self." *Christopher J. Charleton*

Gaming

Gaming can become addictive when used as a means to escape from dealing with life stresses. A neurochemical high is received associated with pursuit and reward especially when gaming with sexual and violent stimuli. Gaming or digital/electronic experiences may also include: interactive virtual sex (digital/electronic enhancement of sexual experience) and anime/hentai (sex cartoon) utilization.

Grooming

Grooming behaviors are those which seem innocent, but are intended to gain someone's trust and therefore to gain an opportunity to generally benefit from someone or for making sexual advances. Both sexual perpetrators and sexual addicts sometimes engage in grooming potential victims or sexual partners.

Intimacy

Intimacy described in the Bible is seen in the Hebrew word "yada," "to know" by experience: to learn, to perceive, to discern, to experience, to know and be known relationally. For intimate relationships to flourish, whether with man or God, we must feel safe to reveal ourselves without holding back or keeping secrets.

Intimacy Disorder

Intimacy disorder results from the core beliefs "I am a bad and worthless person," and "No one will like me as I am." These ideas are foundational to addicts and co-addicts. Those who suffer from either disorder believe that if they tell the truth or express their real emotions, other people won't like them or may even end up hating them and leaving. This fear often means that the people whom we're most afraid of losing, like our spouse, will be the one to whom we are less likely to tell the truth. Intimacy Disorder is a fear- and anxiety-based disorder: Fear that someone will leave us, and the anxiety that we'll be all alone.

Patrick Carnes, a renowned addiction recovery expert states that, "more than 87 percent of patients come from disengaged families — a family environment in which family members are detached, uninvolved, or emotionally absent. All compulsive and addictive behaviors are signs of significant intimacy disorder and the inability to get needs met in healthy ways." http://enrichmentjournal.ag.org/200504/200504_022_internet.cfm.

L.I.F.E. Recovery Model (LRM)

The LRM is a compilation of "Best Practices" for addiction recovery from practitioners, group facilitators and those who have implemented these practices to successfully Live In Freedom Everyday. L.I.F.E. Recovery is committed to continually provide and update the LRM with proven addiction recovery information from a biblical and clinical basis. The LRM was created out of compassion for persons seeking sexual addiction recovery in an ever increasing and diverse market of programs, materials and books of which most offer incomplete or misguided information. The purpose of the LRM is now to provide proven methods for recovery from addictive behavior as well as sexual addiction recovery that unite the recovery strategies of individuals, organizations and ministries to work together, worldwide. Individually, before a "L.I.F.E." of recovery can be experienced one must develop disciplines that pursue wholeness. These disciplines are presented in the LRM, with particular emphasis on the initiatives begun in the First Year of Recovery. When these multiple disciplines are applied consistently they result in healthy intimate relationships where individuals are safe to express feelings and process pain. There is great hope for those who view this model and follow its practices. See our website to view the LRM in its entirety.

http://www.freedomeveryday.org/lrm.

Medicating/Pharmacological Management

Medicating refers to using a substance or behavior to alter mood. Some substances and behaviors can elevate "down" moods such as loneliness, depression or boredom; and some can depress (or lower) moods like anxiety, fear, or stress. Medicating has been called "pharmacological management" in that the person manipulates his own mood, becoming like a pharmacist of his own brain.

Minimizing

Similar to denial (and really a form of it) minimizing literally means attempting to make smaller what is really true. Typically, a person tries to minimize how his destructive behaviors affect himself and others.

Models of Recovery

We recognize two basic approaches or "models" of recovery; the Disease Model and the Trauma or Core Issue Model. The Disease Model places its focus on the behavior of the addict and not on the issues that drive that behavior. This is a typical 12-step approach, in either a secular or Christian setting, involving behavioral skills and disciplines, and related behavior modification techniques. The Trauma/Core Issue Model focuses instead on the issues that are driving the behavior, in recognition that addictive behavior comes from the need to medicate the pain from past wounds. Recovery must go deeper than just change in behavior, and address the wounds that are the source of that pain. Transformation requires that the addict actually gets well, not just sober.

Narcissism

This is a clinical term that is more commonly used to refer to self-centered behavior. Narcissus was a Greek figure who loved looking at his own reflection. "Narcissists" often congratulate themselves on their own accomplishments or give themselves a wide variety of compliments. They seem to be thinking only about themselves and not about others. Their own agenda is the most important. Narcissists often seem very grandiose and self-confident or self-assured, but they really are not. Instead, they are very insecure and concerned about others' approval. Usually, these people have been "narcissistically wounded" - that is, they've experienced life traumas that have damaged their sense of belonging and of being worthy. Narcissists actually lack self-confidence and are trying to bolster themselves.

Neurochemical

All activities of the brain are facilitated by the interaction of chemicals in the brain. What is sometimes called the electrical activity of the brain is based on chemistry, or "neurochemistry." Scientists have identified hundreds of chemicals involved in the process of "communication" among brain cells. Some people are born with genetic predispositions to having problems with the proper balance of these chemicals. Addictive and dysfunctional behavior can also alter the normal state of brain chemistry. Psychiatry is the medical science that seeks to understand the right balance and prescribe medications to correct such disorders.

Objectification

This literally means to view someone who is fully human as an object rather than a person. Sexually, objectification means to see someone as only a physical body and not as a person with a mind and soul. Objectifying is de-humanizing. When we objectify someone, it's easier to lust after that person as just a body to be desired.

Rationalization

This is an excuse or justification. Rationalizations are used to try to explain why something was or wasn't done.

Recovery Plan

A recovery plan is an intentional effort working toward consistent application of multiple disciplines that result in healthy intimate relationships where we are safe to express feelings and processing pain. Before a "L.I.F.E." of recovery can be experienced one must develop disciplines that pursue wholeness, all of which are presented in the LRM (L.I.F.E. Recovery Model) which can be viewed in its entirety on our website, http://www.freedomeveryday.org/lrm.

There are **non-negotiable** aspects for a successful "First Year of Recovery" that are detailed in the LRM. Frequent evaluations of a recovery plan are crucial for long term success, especially at times when fulfillment appears illusive.

Relapse

A relapse is a series of slips that reflect the crossing of emotional and spiritual boundaries. A relapse is an on-going violation of sobriety.

Sexual Anorexia

Like those who struggle with food anorexia inhibit their eating, sexual anorexics avoid sex. Other clinical terms are "inhibited sexual desire" or "disorder of sexual desire." Painful memories (conscious or unconscious) shut down sexual desire or availability. Anorexia is often about anger and/or anxiety. Sex addicts can be sexual with others and anorexic with their spouses. In these cases, guilt, shame, anxiety, or a variety of other factors shut them down sexually within their marriages.

Shame

One of the core beliefs of addicts is "I am a bad and worthless person," which is a shame-based conviction. Shame, though, isn't inherently bad. There can be "healthy shame," which we feel when we know we need God. "Unhealthy shame" occurs when a person's life experiences, like trauma, lead him to believe he doesn't deserve God's love.

In Hebrew, Shame [H954], or to be ashamed, is defined as the confusion, disgrace, embarrassment, dismay, or disappointment that things didn't turn out as expected. Utter defeat pervades the mood, disillusion and a broken spirit will follow.

If shame still exists it hinders full development in Christ. Shame comes from past circumstances and experiences that injure our value. Shame must be vigorously uprooted and we must grieve the "injury" to our value or we cannot grow into the vision (fullness of joy).

Slip

A slip is a one-time violation of sobriety in any form. "Slip is an acronym for "Short Lapse In Progress." A violation of sobriety remains a "short lapse" only if the person learns from it, repents, and grows in understanding as a result.

Sobriety

Most simply sobriety is abstinence from any substance or coping, escaping or medicating behavior with an understanding that deeper core wounds drive the behavior(s) as a means of dealing with core issues. Sobriety is the condition of not having any measurable levels or effects from mood-altering substances or behaviors.

Sobriety for Co-Addicts

As L.I.F.E. Recovery continues to work with those who are in relationship with an addict, we have found that certain behaviors, or the absence of certain behaviors, indicate sobriety for co-addicts and they are listed below.

- No Controlling and Manipulative Behavior
- No Enabling
- No Snooping or Playing the "Detective"
- No Fantasy
- No Transference, Taking on the Addict's Recovery or Behaviors

- No Self-Medicating or Escaping Behavior
- No Surrender of Values or Self
- Appropriate Boundaries and Respect for the Boundaries of Others

Sponsor

A sponsor is the person who is your main accountability partner. The qualities of a sponsor are described in Principle Four, Assignment One. While you will need many people in your accountability group or network, there will be one person who takes charge and helps you direct the show. This person helps you plan your overall healing journey, including meeting attendance, phone calls, counseling, and spiritual direction. He will not necessarily do all of these things, but he'll help you monitor how you are doing in the program. You will need to "submit" to your sponsor's authority and to determine what consequences will be appropriate if you fail to honor your commitments to healing.

Top Line

A "Top Line" is a boundary or behavior that guides or protects our becoming all that God desires us to be. Top Line behaviors support our recovery plan and require taking responsibility for feelings, actions and especially for the protection of our value. For example, spending time with others who are safe and demonstrate, or are learning, healthy boundaries and healthy behaviors would be a Top Line. Top Line behaviors can look like goals or objectives. We might include L.I.F.E. Recovery Group and Christian fellowship as a Top Line as well as studying addiction recovery material or other elements listed in the L.I.F.E. Recovery Model which set us up for successful recovery, each of these could be considered a Top Line. For more information on this process, see Bottom Line.

Trauma

Injury whether physical, emotional, sexual or spiritual to the true value of a person bestowed upon him/her by God to one created in His image.

Trauma Bonding

This is one of the trauma reactions described in Principle One, Assignment Three. It's commonly used to refer to dysfunctional attachments and unhealthy relationships. To be trauma bonded means that two people are attracted to each other because of conscious and unconscious characteristics that remind them of people earlier in their lives who wounded them. The unconscious hope is that attaching to this kind of person will provide a new chance to heal the old wounds. Basically, the hope is that if you keep repeating old behaviors you'll eventually get it right. Sometimes trauma bonding occurs when one person hopes this time to be more in control, to reverse the roles, or to be the one with the power.

Trauma Model Approach to Recovery

The Trauma Model approach to recovery seeks to uncover and heal the core wounds, with the belief that healing will alleviate the craving for the use of a substance or the need to rely dependently upon any behavior for validation or worth.

Addictive behavior is widely understood to be an attempt to medicate the pain of some past trauma or relational wounding that has not been resolved. The original emotional damage thus becomes a core issue, and the fact that it remains unresolved becomes the often subconscious excuse for the relationally and spiritually destructive behavior. The behavioral controls we impose, emotionally and spiritually, on childhood traumas as we mature into adulthood often serve only to rationalize and entrench the addictive behavior. We numb the pain over and over, often with increasing levels of the pain-killing behavior, just to maintain that numbness. Satan is always there to use and intensify that inability to identify and express emotions, and to further disable our ability to have relationship with those we care about or even with God Himself. The principles within this L.I.F.E. Recovery Guide can help you invite Christ into the painful emotions associated with your suffering, and identify those core issues from the past. Jesus himself expressed emotions in very open and often strong ways: He was moved to tears in the Garden, and to righteous anger in clearing the money changers from the Temple. Many of us have not been taught how to process and express such feelings. In order to heal, we must be able to express emotions in a manner that is consistent and constructive, and to deal with those core wounds in a safe environment such as a L.I.F.E. Recovery Group, where real relationships are built—open, transparent and accountable.

Trigger, General

There are two basic kinds of triggers in our program. Any stimulus that is seen, heard, felt, smelled, tasted, remembered, or fantasized about that creates emotional and spiritual feelings of anxiety, fear, loneliness, boredom, depression, or anger is a general trigger. Often, general triggers are also referred to as "emotional triggers."

Trigger, Sexual

It is generally assumed that the word trigger refers to the stimulation of inappropriate sexual desire or action. Any stimulus that is seen, heard, felt, smelled, tasted, remembered, or fantasized about that creates sexual desire or action (even if only in the brain) is a sexual trigger.

We're conscious of many possible sexual triggers, such as looking at pornography or an attractive person. Memories of past sexual experiences (sometimes referred to as euphoric recall) can trigger sexual thoughts. Music, such as a particular song, can have the same effect. Other triggers may be more unconscious. They can be based on life experiences that we don't always consciously remember. Certain words or actions, certain expressions or tones of voice, certain times of the year or events, certain music, and certain sexual behavior can all trigger emotions or reactions. One key to identifying a trigger is to discern if your emotional reaction seems out of proportion to the event that's taking place. When that happens, your unconscious memory may be taking you to old places in ways you don't always realize. Have you ever had someone say, "You're overreacting"? The reason behind your "overreaction" is probably some unconscious trigger.

A Final Word On Words

Words are words. Definitions and understandings change over the years. It's never a good idea to argue about definitions. They aren't something to live or die for. Words are simply tools to help us communicate. If there's a disagreement about some term, come to a group consensus and move forward.

In addition to these terms that we've defined, your group may encounter many others that we haven't included. Please contact L.I.F.E. Recovery with terms you'd like to know about, have a good definition for, or simply think should be included in future editions of this *L.I.F.E. Recovery Guide.*

Reflective Listening Worksheet

This sheet may be used individually or as a Facilitator in listening/guiding another group member.

1. Choose an appropriate emotion and insert it in the space provided then finish filling out the sentence.

2. With the objective of protecting your value in God's Purpose ask, "What do I need?" *(to be heard and understood, affirmed, blessed, safe, touched, chosen, or included) from "Seven Desires of the Heart"- Dr. Mark Laaser*

3. List your next action steps to get that need met.

4. Then process this worksheet with an accountability partner.

   To achieve clarity during an emotional muddle, use a single worksheet to process each emotion.

5. I feel _____ about _____ because _____

6. I need _____

7. My next action steps are _____

FEELINGS TABLE with INTENSIFIERS

Glad	Sad	Angry	Confused	Scared	Weak
Amused	Apathetic	Aggravated	Anxious	Afraid	Ashamed
Calm	Awful	Annoyed	Awkward	Anxious	Bored
Capable	Bad	Critical	Baffled	Concerned	Defenseless
Cheerful	Blue	Disgusted	Bothered	Fearful	Discouraged
Confident	Crushed	Enraged	Crazy	Frightened	Embarrassed
Content	Depressed	Envious	Dazed	Horrified	Exhausted
Energetic	Despondent	Fed Up	Disorganized	Insecure	Fragile
Excited	Disappointed	Frustrated	Disoriented	Intimidated	Frail
Fantastic	Dissatisfied	Furious	Distracted	Jumpy	Guilty
Grateful	Disturbed	Hateful	Disturbed	Lonely	Helpless
Happy	Down	Impatient	Embarrassed	Nervous	Horrible
Healthy	Gloomy	Irate	Helpless	Panicky	Ill
Hopeful	Glum	Irritated	Numb	Shaky	Impotent
Optimistic	Hopeless	Mad	Paralyzed	Shy	Inadequate
Peaceful	Hurt	Mean	Puzzled	Stunned	Insecure
Proud	Lonely	Murderous	Struck	Tense	Lifeless
Powerful	Lost	Outraged	Surprised	Terrified	Lost
Relaxed	Low	Rage	Trapped	Threatened	Overwhelmed
Relieved	Miserable	Resentful	Troubled	Timid	Powerless
Satisfied	Painful	Spiteful	Uncertain	Uneasy	Quiet
Secured	Sorry	Sore	Uncomfortable	Unsafe	Useless

Comparison of Concepts
L.I.F.E. Recovery's 7 Principles to 12-Step

Principle One
Loss of control of life and unmanageability of addiction behaviors.
See Step 1

Principle Two
I believe in God.
See Steps 2, 3
I surrender to Christ.

Principle Three
Make a list of sin and weaknesses,
See Steps 4

and confess (to God and) to a person of spiritual authority.
See Step 5

Principle Four
We seek accountability and build our character as children of God.
See Steps 6, 7, 10

Principle Five
We explore the damage we have done, accept responsibility, and make amends for our wrongs.
See Steps 8, 9

Principle Six
In fellowship with others we develop honest, intimate relationships where we celebrate our progress and continue to address our weaknesses.
See Steps 5, 6, 7, 11

Principle Seven
As we live in integrity and wholeness, we carry the message of Christ's healing power to those who still struggle, and we pursue a vision of God's purpose for our lives.
See Steps 11, 12

Step One
Powerless over my addiction and life has become unmanageable

Step Two
"came to believe in a Higher Power (Jesus Christ)

Step Three
"turn my will and life over to God" (Christ)

Step Four (Knowing self)
"make a searching and fearless moral inventory of self" (the wrongs done to me – this would be identifying the traumatic experiences that have shaped by thinking [core beliefs] and the resulting emotional pain; as well as the wrongs done by me). Step 4 establishes awareness and knowledge of life experiences that have formed the foundation and the direction of "management" of my life resulting in the "mess of the moment" -- this "moment" being the point in time in which I have decided to change the course of my life.

Step Five
"Admitted to God, to ourselves, and to another human being the exact nature of our wrongs." Edward Sellner, in Hazelden Foundation's interpretation of "The Twelve Steps of Alcoholics Anonymous" states that "a good fifth step starts with the fourth."
Admitting (confession) to self is necessary to the addict taking ownership and responsibility for their addiction irrespective of the "roots."
Step Five is an ongoing process.

Step Six
"We're (I prefer the use of the word "are" since this is an on-going process) entirely ready to have God remove all these defects of character."

Step Seven
"Humbly ask Him to remove our shortcomings."

Step Eight
"Made a list of all persons we had harmed, and became willing to make amends to them all."

Step Nine
Made direct amends to such people wherever possible, except where to do so would injure them or others.

Step Ten
Continued to take personal inventory, and when we were wrong, promptly admitted it.

Step Eleven
Sought through prayer and meditation to improve our conscious contact with God, as we understood Him, praying only for knowledge of His will for us, and the power to carry that out.

Step Twelve
Having had a spiritual awakening as the result of these steps, we tried to carry this message to alcoholics, and to practice these principles in all our affairs

RESOURCES

A number of good resources are available to aid Christians in their journey of transformation. Through both printed material and the World Wide Web, those who seek to live in freedom everyday can find information and inspiration. A primary source of additional understanding are the programs and materials offered by L.I.F.E. Recovery International.

Because it's impossible to maintain an up-to-date list of any of these resources in this printed L.I.F.E. Recovery Guide, please visit our website for current suggestions of where to turn for help in the areas of addiction, co-addiction, trauma, and recovery.

www.freedomeveryday.org

ABOUT THE AUTHOR

Dr. Ralph Spiller is a US Navy retired Chief Warrant Officer with a distinguished 21-year Naval career where, along with his primary duties, he was also the Drug and Alcohol Programs Advisor in the early days of military efforts to address chemical substance abuse issues among the sailors and officers of the Navy. Retiring from the Navy in 1980, Dr. Spiller completed a theological education that prepared him for his next venture as a prison chaplain where he encountered individuals with serious histories of chemical substance abuse, as well as trauma issues of early childhood sexual abuse and other forms of family abuse, the consequences of which led to lifestyles of bad choices in their efforts to cope with the traumas of these previous life experiences. Counseling these individuals presented challenges that led him to graduate school where he received a Masters Degree in Mental Health Counseling. Dr. Spiller engaged in counseling children, adolescents, and their families who had similar life experiences in family life that led to the children being placed in the foster care system. He has also treated juvenile and adult sex offenders and adult sex addicts, as well as outpatient chemical substance abuse clients in a community mental health/substance abuse clinic treating dual diagnosed clients, and outpatient chemical substance clients for the Federal Bureau of Prisons. He held a private practice for over 10 years.

In addition to his counseling ministry, Dr. Spiller has bi-vocationally pastored 5 churches. He continues to maintain a very active teaching ministry in his present church. He presently serves as the President and Chairman of the Board of Directors for The Christian 12-Step Ministries, Incorporated, which has a presence in prisons in all 50 states and 7 foreign countries with their textbook/workbook having been translated into 5 foreign languages.

Dr. Spiller received his PhD from Maimonides University in North Miami, FL with a focus in the forensic sexual disorders. His dissertation is entitled, *The Unspoken Addictions: Sex, Love, and Romance.* His Masters Degree was conferred by Stetson University, Deland, FL, and his Bachelor in Theology is from The Baptist College of Florida.

Dr. Spiller and his wife, Barbara, have been married 48 years, and they have 2 daughters, six grandchildren, and 1 great-grandchild. It truly has been "a wonderful life."

L.I.F.E. RECOVERY INTERNATIONAL

- *Living In Freedom Everyday* -

Mission

The mission of L.I.F.E. Recovery International is to encourage, empower and equip God's people to live everyday in freedom from the addictive condition.

Vision

L.I.F.E. Recovery's vision is to have a L.I.F.E. Recovery Group within 20 miles of anyone one needing help.

Services

L.I.F.E. Recovery offers Christ-centered recovery materials, and relationally oriented support groups that incorporate spiritual discipline, small group accountability, and ongoing prayer and support for those struggling in addiction. L.I.F.E. also provides training for support group facilitators and others with a heart to help people in these areas.

Ministry Founders

Bob Hale, MBA, President
Johna Hale, MPA, M.A. Executive Director

Contact Information

L.I.F.E. Recovery International
P.O. Box 952317
Lake Mary, FL 32795

www.freedomeveryday.org

mailto:info@freedomeveryday.org

Toll-free 866-408-LIFE

Made in the USA
Columbia, SC
14 May 2020